MISCELLANY OF LIGHTING & STAGECRAFT

Michael Hall
Julie Harper

ENTERTAINMENT TECHNOLOGY PRESS

Reference Series

MISCELLANY OF LIGHTING & STAGECRAFT

Michael Hall and Julie Harper

 et press

Entertainment Technology Press

Miscellany of Lighting & Stagecraft

© Michael Hall and Julie Harper

First edition published April 2013
by Entertainment Technology Press Ltd
The Studio, High Green, Great Shelford, Cambridge CB22 5EG
Internet: www.etnow.com

ISBN 978 1 904031 68 0

A title within the
Entertainment Technology Press Reference Series
Series editor: John Offord

CODE / MLS-04/13

PREFACE

Our brief was to produce a book that would help schools, colleges, amateurs, technicians and all interested in practical theatre and performance to understand, in an entertaining and informative way, the key backstage skills. We decided that, rather than write the book entirely ourselves, we would ask our friends and other professionals to share their own special knowledge and expertise. We have interspersed this with diversions of historic interest and anecdotes from those practising at the front line of our industry.

When we look at the array of skills shown by our contributors, it confirms that we could not have written such a masterly series of treatises on such a diversity of subjects ourselves. We also believe that many of them are unique in setting out skills and advice previously not set to print.

The Cast List with its collection of personal profiles illustrates, in miniature, the wonderful skillset and experience that have gone into this book and we are deeply grateful to all our contributors for the richness and diversity of their offerings.

We extend our heartfelt thanks to Fred Foster for adding his Foreword which we feel encapsulates perfectly our intentions in putting together this book, and to Ken Billington for his excellent American Overview (p161). Lastly, and most importantly, we hope this Miscellany will inform and entertain you.

Michael and Julie

"Jeu d'orgue" at the Paris Opera. Charles Nuitter, Le Nouvel Opera, (Paris: 1875).

FOREWORD

Fred Foster is president of Electronic Theatre Controls, inc.

In the fall of 1939, a young man named Jean Hodgin lit the first production ever held at the University of Wisconsin's brand-new Memorial Union Theater. The show was *The Taming of the Shrew*, starring Alfred Lunt and Lynne Fontaine, and Jean had stayed on an extra year at University just to do the project.

After school and service in World War II, Jean worked in small theaters and toured a production of *Porgy and Bess* through 26 war-ravaged cities circling the Mediterranean. Later he was a cameraman in the nascent television industry and eventually returned to Wisconsin to become the houseman at the Union Theater.

I met Jean in 1975, when I was a young student at the University. By that time, he was a crusty old stagehand. When we would load a show out of his theater, throwing flats into the alley as garbage, he would be out there in the dark with his hammer, salvaging nails from the lumber, grumbling on about how "kids these days don't value anything". Then, when we were loading in our next show and needed only one more four-penny nail, Jean would reach into one of his countless coffee cans and give us one. It might be bent and rusty, but he had the four-penny nail we needed.

I had read about technical theater in books but I really learned my stagecraft from Jean. He taught me how to lash flats together and how to rig a batten with hemp line and sandbags. He taught me to run the old Genarco followspot and how you had to cool the fuses with freeze spray so they wouldn't blow during the show. And most importantly, he instilled in me the most important value of the theater: *the show must go on*. For many years, while we were just starting ETC (Electronic Theatre Controls, Inc.), I worked as a stage carpenter, electrician and rigger. I worked alongside Jean on many shows in many theaters utilizing the craft that I had learned from him. I still hold my IATSE union card today but must admit that I have not worked a show in many years. Every day, however, I apply that most important lesson that Jean taught me to our business: *the show must go on*. Our products must work and if they don't, we must do everything possible to fix them.

In these pages, Michael Hall and Julie Harper have gathered a trove of technical theater knowledge, presenting it in a unique format. Whatever your area of interest – lighting, scenery, makeup, stage management, even theater planning – you will find valuable information. Interspersed throughout, you will also find fascinating stories about our business. Broadway LD Ken Billington describes the evolution and development of lighting design as a recognized art. Architect Roger Joyce tells how his love for the theater started at the Medway Little Theatre in Rochester and how that passion continues today. Paule Constable writes about gobos – but is really sharing her views on light, nature and seeing. Chris Clark sums up his piece by saying that the "act of scene painting must be enjoyed." There are gems like these throughout this book. Seek them and you will develop a deeper understanding not just of what we do in theater but *why* we do it. You may find 'the lesson' and the wisdom of a mentor like Jean Hodgin, which will stay with you throughout your career and life.

Fred Foster

CONTENTS

CAST LIST
NOT IN ORDER OF APPEARANCE

Ken Billington apprenticed with Broadway's most successful lighting designers and designed his first New York production in 1973. Since then he has designed the lighting for nearly 100 Broadway shows, as well as numerous nightclub acts, television specials, operas around the world, and such spectaculars as the Radio City Music Hall Christmas show (27 years!).

Nick Bromley After training at London's Central School of Speech and Drama, Nick worked as Company and Stage Manager for many West End productions, including Starlight Express and The King and I. He has been assistant to Orson Welles and is currently Master of the Drury Lane Theatrical Fund.

Jason Barnes trained at Central School before embarking on a 45 year Theatre career encompassing the roles of stage and production manager, consultant, visiting artist Trenton College New Jersey, lighting designer, author and visiting lecturer principal UK Drama Schools. Boards: British Theatre Association, Shakespeare's Rose, Mander & Mitchenson, The Theatres Trust. Fellow Guildhall School, Rose Bruford College, ABTT. National Theatre production manager Cottesloe 1977 – 2009. London Theatre Studies tutor/director Samford University Alabama.

David Brooks is a director of Technical Marketing Ltd – a company that specialises in offering a total capability in marketing services to manufacturers and service providers of entertainment technology. He has been advising British Harlequin plc on marketing strategy and providing PR services to them for the last ten years.

Sharon D. Calcutt was going to be a musician and then … she got caught up in theatre and never looked back. Ten years on she is a well regarded stage manager in the industry. She writes for *The Stage*, and she teaches the next generation in London's leading drama schools.

Chris Clark is a scenic artist with over 40 years' experience in realising theatre designers' stage imagery. Since 1989, in professional partnership with his wife Liz, the couple have been assigned to paint scenery by major UK and international theatre, opera and dance companies and received various scenic commissions from rock stars to royalty.

Andrew Collier is a director of Technical Marketing Ltd – a company that specialises in offering a total capability in marketing services to manufacturers and service providers of entertainment technology. He is also a member of the Executive Committee of the Association of Lighting Designers and editor of its magazine, *Focus*.

Paule Constable is a UK based lighting designer working internationally in theatre and opera. She has designed for the RSC, Glyndebourne, the Royal Opera House, New York Metropolitan Opera, the ENO and the National Theatre with productions that include the award-winning *His Dark Materials* and the internationally acclaimed production of *War Horse*.

Ian Dow retired as an engineering manager with BBC TV Outside Broadcasts where he lit shows including Dr Who, Animal Hospital, and State Banquets at Windsor Castle. In his spare time he teaches lighting to young technicians in his local Youth Theatre, and is a signalman on a steam railway.

Philip L. Edwards has been involved in theatre lighting for over 50 years. From 1966 he spent seven years with BBC television followed by the Royal Northern College of Music designing lighting for most of the College's productions until July 2010. He now freelances.

Kevin Fitz-Simons discovered theatre lighting at the age of 20 and spent the next 30 years of his working life as part of the Industry – either as practitioner, educator or supplier – all over the UK and abroad. Away from his current role at AC Entertainment Technologies Ltd he lives a quiet life as a minority with his wife and two daughters and a bass trombone.

Alasdair Flint operated a large scenery building company for 20 years, specialising in the construction of theatre and opera scenery. Now he runs a company which supplies the entertainment industry with backstage hardware. The company employs 40 staff and exports worldwide.

Adam Grater has lit concert artistes and theatre productions, U-boats and electric arc furnaces. Collaboration with lighting designer David Hersey led to the formation of DHA Designs in 1988. It is now one of the world's leading lighting design consultancies.

Mark Jonathan worked in the lighting department at Glyndebourne from 1978 until 1992 when he became head of lighting at the National Theatre, London. Since 2003 he has worked as a freelance lighting designer of plays, musicals, opera and ballet in the UK, USA, Europe and Asia.

Roger Joyce is a chartered architect with a life-long passion for amateur theatre, from secondary school, via Rochester's Medway Little Theatre and now Folkestone's FHODs, for whom he directed *Much Ado About Nothing*. He believes this opportunity to join an RSC initiative will help to improve the general quality of productions, and encourage others to join the group.

James Laws is a Fellow of The Association of Lighting Designers. He was resident lighting designer at Windsor, Farnham and Basingstoke in the 1970s. He specialises in lighting musicians and teaching lighting history, demonstrating candlelight. A journalist and photographer, he provides permanent lighting for churches and lives in Suffolk.

Durham Marenghi has designed the lighting for a wide variety of theatre, opera, dance, trade, architectural, concert and television productions and is the first British lighting designer to have lit the Opening and Closing Ceremonies of an Olympic Games. He designed the lighting for the critically acclaimed Diamond Jubilee Concert in June 2012 for which he was awarded a Royal Television Society Craft Award. He also designs the New Year's Eve Light and Fireworks show from the London Eye each year.

Nick Moran's work over 25 years has ranged from fringe theatre to stadium rock, in roles that include lighting designer, programmer, project manager and production electrician. Nick is senior lecturer in lighting and head of undergraduate design at Royal Central School of Speech & Drama in London.

Matt Prentice trained as a lighting designer and production electrician at The Bristol Old Vic Theatre Royal where he continued to work until turning freelance. A role as lighting tutor at Mountview Academy of Theatre Arts saw him progress to head of lighting before moving to the RADA as head of lighting in 2006. Freelance lighting credits include an award for Best Lighting Design by the Critics Circle Awards in 2006 for The National Theatre's production of *Faust.*

Declan Randall has a degree in Stage Lighting Design and Arts Administration and over the past 18 years has designed the lighting for more than 250 productions, his work being seen all around the world. Declan has also won several awards for lighting design.

Jackie Staines has made contributions to this book based on her experiences working at Scarborough's Stephen Joseph Theatre as chief technician and resident lighting designer. Now working for Entertainment Technology Press as technical editor, she has enjoyed compiling and contributing to this book. Like Roger Joyce, Jackie first 'trod the boards' at Medway Little Theatre in Rochester!

Richard Thompson practised as a dentist for 20 years, whilst being an active amateur actor/singer. He started lighting plays in Bingley in 1979 and since then has designed and run various musicals and dance shows at varied venues from Bingley Arts Centre (now run by Bingley Little Theatre) via various halls to the Bradford Alhambra.

John Toogood trained at Bristol Old Vic Theatre School, and was stage manager for seven years at The Liverpool Playhouse. From 1972 he worked as company manager in London for prominent producers, including the young Cameron Mackintosh. He ran the Prince Edward Theatre for ten years before moving to the Old Vic and then Lincoln's City Hall. John was chairman of the SMA between 1984-1993 and now works as a freelance journalist, radio contributor jazz promoter and compere.

Paul de Ville trained as a stage technician and lighting designer. He spent 23 years at Theatre Projects, Lighting Technology and Lightfactor advising designers in theatre, film, television and display lighting. After a three year sabbatical he joined Rosco in 2008.Throughout this time he worked on several commercial and entertainment projects as a lighting designer.

Donald Walker worked from 1949 in stage management, including lavish Harold Fielding productions, some with the Coliseum triple revolve. He set up the Curtain Theatre at the Toynbee Hall for the LCC and is well known as a theatre historian and as a world authority on early stage technology.

Mark White has been a West End chief electrician, buildings and technical manager for a West End theatres group, a technical manager at the Royal Opera House, during the Covent Garden redevelopment 1995-99. Currently employed by Electronic Theatre Controls Ltd, Mark is also chairman of the Association of British Theatre Technicians (ABTT).

Early film in theatre – we wonder if the film format came from the proscenium arch dimensions.

INTRODUCTION

There are many skills needed for staging theatre and entertainment, and it is becoming ever more complex. Every day we see examples on television, film, stage and live events which form our impressions of how it should be presented, but not how it can be achieved. We have taken advantage of the knowledge and experience of those trained professionals working in these environments to give an insight into some of the skills and resources that bring these spectacles into being.

Our intention with this book is to provide a Miscellany that is not ordered or categorised in strict fashion, but rather encourages the reader to flick through or dip into it, finding nuggets of information and anecdotes to entertain, inspire and engender curiosity; to invite further research or exploration and generally encourage people to enter our industry and find out for themselves.

The road into the entertainment industry is seldom a well-mapped route but an adventure that can be approached from any number of angles and spread out into an infinite number of possibilities. We invite you to use this book as a springboard from which to launch yourself into the realms of possibility!

As lighting people, we understand there is a bias towards lighting in this edition, but we invite you to submit your own stories in anticipation of a second edition!

Loie Fuller – The skirt, or prismatic dance, a development of the Serpentine dance: Note the followspots, one with a colour wheel, projector understage and in front of the footlights.

STAGECRAFT

Your School Needs a New Venue

"We don't have a theatre"

"There isn't a hall for concerts"

"Students shouldn't be expected to have to dance in there"

There may be existing buildings which need improvement or there might be the need for new construction.

Before being able to start anything you must be absolutely confident of your 'Vision' for the project. To establish this 'Vision' all those who have any interest in the proposed facilities must go through a comprehensive process to consider all the needs, aspirations and possibilities they have for what is proposed.

From the outcome of this process will come the essential priorities which will become the 'Vision' for the scheme.

Some of the issues you need to consider and understand are:

- How many types of performance you wish to stage, e.g. drama, musical theatre, opera, dance?
- Is there a need to present music and concert performances?
- How flexible do you wish the space to be?
- Do you wish to have different stage arrangements, e.g. end-on, thrust, in-the-round, traverse, promenade…?
- Do you wish to be able to have a front-of-house and/or box office operation?
- Will you wish to gain a licence for entertainments?
- Will there be community use of the venue?
- Will there be commercial use of the venue?
- Will it need to be independent of other school accommodation or have an independent use during the school day?

In how much of the venue operation do you wish pupils to have an opportunity to be involved, e.g. performance, stage management, set construction, make-up, wardrobe, lighting, sound, front of house, box office?

Who will support and supervise on-going, community and commercial use, e.g. theatre manager, box office manager, resident stage manager, theatre technician?

How much do you wish to integrate the venue into broader curriculum delivery; will it have a role as a lecture or demonstration theatre?

Will curriculum areas other than the performing arts be involved with the space, e.g. Business Studies, Art and Design, Engineering and Technology?

What opportunities exist for improved or extended accessibility and the development of best practice beyond statutory compliance?

When your needs are clear, then you can approach a Theatre Consultancy (See Index) with an outline brief and a budget.

Theatreplan

BENEATH THE STAGE—TRAPS AND PLATFORMS.

The Amateur Director

My fascination for Theatre began at a very early age. My parents tell me that as kids, we staged puppet shows (I still have Mr Punch, though his rubber face is perishing) and mounted variety shows for the families on troop ships returning from the middle east in the 1950s.

It was natural, then, that I should join a Youth Group at the Medway Little Theatre in Rochester when my father's last posting brought him to Chatham, and that, when attending Art School in Canterbury, I should form the crazy gang who staged entertainments for the end of term concerts. At MLTC, I learned the craft of stage design, and watched lighting technicians winding huge ex-cinema dimmer boards, to achieve magical lighting effects. Thyristers followed, and our lighting plots became ever more ambitious.

Currently, I am a member of a 100-year old amateur group on the south coast in Folkestone, who, over the years, have performed in the Pleasure Garden Theatre, Cinemas, Edwardian Tea-rooms and their own tiny 100-seat converted Church Theatre – as well as a huge seaside concert hall, all of which offered their own challenges for setting, lighting and performance.

Some years ago, the group bought a redundant Garrison Church from the Defence Estates, and set about turning this a cathedral of a place into a fully equipped 300-seat Community Theatre Centre, complete with state of the art lighting equipment 'acquired' from the Wembley Conference Centre, and for the first time, full flying facilities...

It is here that we rose the to the challenge of the RSC's 'Open Stages' project to have as many amateur groups throughout the country performing Shakespeare, as part of the Cultural Olympiad, through 2011/12. This is an area of theatre that many us felt had been neglected, so it was a timely, and potentially very exciting catalyst, for us to get involved.

As director, I chose to conduct a series of workshops, to engage with members of the Society, but also the wider community, in the hope that a truly democratic production would emerge. After several months, we had chosen *Much Ado*, and decided that it should be staged relatively traditionally, so as not to challenge ourselves, or to test the appetite of our potential audience too much.

The RSC project is arranged round regional centres, and ours is The Questors, Ealing, where we were obligated to attend a 'skills exchange' weekend of workshops as a condition of remaining in the project. Here, we saw how the pro's do it, and described our own experiences, that were many and varied, depending on the strengths of the various groups, and the resources they had at their disposal.

The role of 'director' probably has as many forms as there are amateur companies, but on our case, it is more a case of twisting arms, and getting others involved, than it is to convene a meeting of the 'tech crew', and to design the show. Casting alone is a necessity – it you don't have your strong principals, it is going to be an uphill struggle. Then there's costume. Although we have accumulated an extensive wardrobe, the budget isn't there to go out to hire 20-odd costumes in, so the director is engaged in 'conversations' with others.

Clearly, when you come up with an idea for a production, and 'shape' emerges somewhere in your imagination, straight away, you are plotting moves that depend on the certain knowledge that the set will appear – but again, scant resources (both human and financial) will dictate what you get. As director, I knocked up a quick model, based on the equipment I knew existed in the workshop, including two useful 8ft x 5ft two-storey trucks that had been made for some panto many years ago. Then, I am thinking of a lighting plot, and ambitious changes of scene are created by manipulating the available lighting. Our stage area is huge, some 31ft x 36ft, having

been the narthex of this great church, and I look to ranging from a cyclorama flooded with Sicilian light at one point, to the creation of a night-time lantern-lit 'street' across the forestage for the arrest of the villains at the beginning of the second half of the play – and from a daylit chamber for the dressing of the bride, to a gloomy chapel with the family tomb back-lit with a gobo lancet window.

In our company, the director stays in constant touch with the Performance and Planning committee, and the theatre manager, to arrange his publicity campaign, his sponsorship and eventually the programme.

Roger Joyce

WORKING FLY-GALLERY.

A Snapshot of an Amateur Theatre Company Production

FHODS – The Folkestone and Hythe Operatic and Dramatic Society – staged Much Ado About Nothing in November 2012, and here is a brief account of the event. Their production embodies much of the work this book deals with, and enables a quality production for a live audience.

The FHODS celebrates its Centenary in 2013. The Society was originally part of the Little Theatre Guild, and based in Sandgate, near Folkestone, Kent. When, in 2001, St Marks, a Grade II listed church in the neighbouring army barracks was put up for sale (the only military left was a battalion of Ghurkas), FHODS put in their sealed bid and came out as the lucky winner. The church, built in 1941, was the largest Garrison church in the UK.

Since then work has been, and continues to be, carried out to convert it to a theatre. It is registered as a charity, and aims to be a community theatre, with space hired out to other societies to help the upkeep costs. It is called the Tower Theatre – the church tower could be seen from France, and during the war, the Germans tried to bomb it, but failed. The Society is one of the few amateur theatre companies in the UK to own their own theatre.

On the evening of our visit, all the signs were promising: a well presented website, ticketing online, a large car park and a welcoming foyer and bar area – more welcoming I think than some other recent theatres. The auditorium seats nearly 300 in comfortable seats, all raked and with no poor sightlines. The stage has a proscenium arch, but for this production the orchestra pit was covered, giving a deep forestage extending at the same level to the first row of seating, giving an intimate almost courtyard feel to the theatre. Interesting – Tyrone Guthrie who was champion of thrust stages believed that Shakespeare could not be acted in a proscenium arch theatre, but demanded presentation almost in-the-round.

There is a workshop attached and an extensive storage area. There are adequate dressing rooms and a green room.

The stage is 10m by 8m from the proscenium arch to the back wall and cyclorama. The height to the proscenium arch is 7.5m. The lighting equipment and sound systems were built up from many sources – some lighting from the nearby Canterbury Marlowe theatre before its recent closure and rebuild (funded by Canterbury City Council) and some of the sound system from Wembley. Lighting control is a Light Factory V2.8 system. There are 104 dimming channels, each with a maximum 2kW load.

A permanent fixed lighting rig includes front of house six ADB Vision 1.2kW profile spots and eight ADB Vision Fresnels, four per side on vertical booms. An interesting additional stock of lanterns include Strand followspots, ETC Source Four 575W profile spots, PARcans, CCT Silhouettes, Strand Harmonys, Preludes through to PATT 23s, and various effects projectors – a mini history package of stage lighting.

Sound control is by an Allen & Heath GL2400 24-channel sound console. There are also CD players, a mini-disk player and a range of Shure, Wharfedale and Sennheiser mics. Speakers are discreetly sited FOH and midway in the auditorium – even a subdued spoken aside was fully audible, without distortion.

The FHODS use the Tower as a receiving theatre for visiting companies but *Much Ado About Nothing* was their own production. The RSC has a new project aiming to "embrace, develop, and celebrate amateur theatre", and this production was part of the *World Shakespeare Festival* under the auspices of the RSC Open Stages Project. It involved a programme of Skills Sharing events and Directors Workshops, held at the Questors Theatre in Ealing.

Ian Wainwright, Producer of the RSC Open Stages, said: "The RSC wants to lead a step change in the relationship with the amateur sector, to recognise its rich traditions ... and to leave a significant legacy." The RSC producer who ran the Skills Events unexpectedly attended the first night, indicating he liked what he saw, costume designs, the language skills, lighting.

Although the theatre does have tabs, this was an open stage. The set was dominated by a well-made wooden balcony, carpenter produced; it will be stored for future use, and the floor a well painted simulation of cobbles.

Roger Joyce (see page 28) as director made a model of the set to show the lighting techies, but by happy chance, Adam Grater, a professional lighting designer of international repute (see his website www.dhadesign. com) lives in Hythe (see page 91 for his views on schools) and I introduced Adam to Roger. Result: the generation of community spirit, Adam designed the lighting, loaned kit, had colour and gobos given by Rosco – a well lit play, and subtle changes of intensity, balance and colour marked each scene and act change.

Adam gave us an account of his experience. "The first step I take in lighting any production is to work out how to hang the available rig in a basic cover so the entire stage can properly be lit.

"I generally like to have a cool and a warm front light coming in from both sides, and a complementary set of back lights.

"Then I take a look at the setting of the play. In Much Ado there is a requirement for bright Italian sun, evening and night looks, so the rig will also need another set of backlights to help give a night feel. These requirements are then 'divided by the equipment available' giving the number of acting areas that the stage can be divided into, using profiles from the front of the house and Fresnels over the stage.

In this case, we managed six areas, downstage left, centre and right, and upstage left, centre and right, and there is also the walkway on the top of the set where some old Patt 123s proved to be invaluable.

We had a cyc (using a recycled grey gauze) so we had to hire in some floods and, as we had been given a glass moon gobo, we managed to resurrect an old Harmony profile for the 'Watch'.

The house also had a bunch of PARcans which gave some useful cross-light and backlight effects for the church and chapel scenes and we had a pretty good-looking rig, albeit being somewhat reduced when one of the racks caught fire at the beginning of the technical!"

Finely chosen 16th Century music was organised from within the Society; it was perfect, well-cued, and with good sound quality.

The cast presented well, were convincing and happy and the audience of 200 or more were responsive and appreciative.

Roger Joyce has had a video made of the show and is having a local company edit it down to highlights, with still inserts, with a copy to all involved. Nice touch!

So much effort and fulfilment for so many people with different skills in a community – what more can you ask?"

Michael Hall

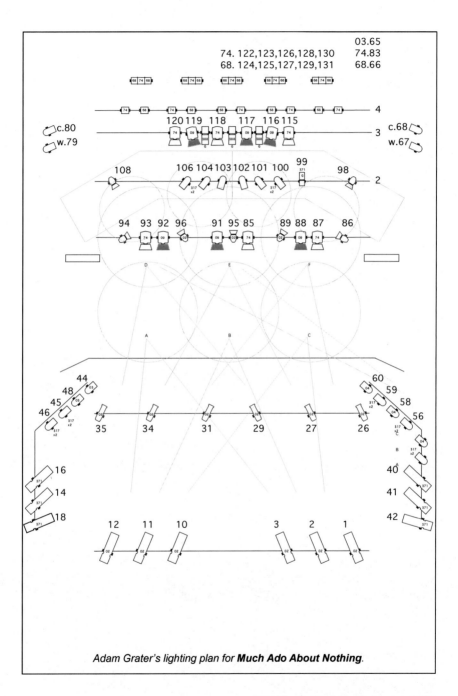

Adam Grater's lighting plan for **Much Ado About Nothing**.

A Stage Manager is Like a Boy Scout – Always Prepared

Early in 1981 when Ken Campbell was artistic director of The Everyman Theatre Liverpool he brought to the Theatre a vibrant piece of performance theatre called Lucky Strike.

"A man rushes into a deserted warehouse in North Africa, pursued by cops. He has a gun, a briefcase and a gut wound. He waits, tense, gun ready. The cop sirens disappear. He looks around, he slowly walks forward, trips over a low stack of bales, falls, his briefcase crashes open littering the warehouse with thousands of US dollar bills. He rushes to collect his money, his gut wound making it very difficult for him to move. He sits back for a moment, produces a pack of Luckys, takes one, sees he has only one match, puts it away. He looks at the strewn money. The police sirens can be heard approaching again. He makes a superhuman effort to collect his money, gun ready to fire.

"Visions of his unfaithful moll and his partner in crime and their betrayal of him repeatedly collide in his crazed mind as he replays these last moments of his life. Flashbacks, flash-forwards, fantasy sequences, nightmares, surrealist imaginings, all collide to repeat a single scene over and over

"Put out the fire before it gets a good hold, and thus save life and property" – the slogan from a Harden Star Grenade advertisement. From The Illustrated London News, June 19th 1886, p.657

and over again with variations, extensions, illusions and hallucinations. Action packed, with very minimal dialogue and a wall to wall ear shattering soundtrack, this tense 70 minutes of jealousy, violence and rage collide in a wild frenzy of choreographed pain, lost love and lost dreams."

The Everyman cast was two old stagers and a newcomer playing the Moll who was not versed in the ways and rules of theatre life.

As the director was the also the writer and with an international profile a fair amount of budget was given over to the show. All the gents suits were tailored for them and the Moll had bespoke silk lingerie as part of her costume.

The first night was a roaring success and after the hard work cast and crew set about partying with a vengeance. Our Moll enjoying her costume so much didn't change and proceeded to party on.

Come the second night at the Hour call, no Moll was in the theatre. The ASM was detailed to try and locate her from the contact numbers we had (this was a time before the mobile phone). The Half was called and still no Moll, and as she was a local the resourceful ASM was now trying to locate her through the network of her friends and family.

The Five was called and through the theatre discussions were held as to what we could tell the full house and the consequences, when in comes the Moll still in her show costume.

Relief all round: the show would only be five minutes late up, the ASM was attempting to get the Moll on stage ready for Beginners and was checking props and costume when the Moll confessed that she was no longer wearing the show lingerie. Making an instant decision, the ASM, told her to go on in her own.

Problem: She wasn't wearing any!

"Ah!", said the ASM.

There was no time to get anything from wardrobe and no wardrobe cover on the show so in the spirit of the "the show must go on" the ASM stepped into the toilet to remove her own, just as the Moll's boyfriend appeared backstage with the costume lingerie.

The Moral of the Tale:

After you've done you pre-show checks, check you have clean underwear as you may never know when for Art's Sake they may be required of you!

Kevin Fitz-Simons

Effects of Yesteryear

The Rain

The crying Baby

The Thunder

Bloodhounds in full cry.

Stage Management

Stage Management is not one of the obviously glamorous areas of theatrical activity. However the role of the stage manager is vitally important, as the preparation and running of the whole show depends on it.

Stage management can be easily summed up as a flair for the management of people, things and events. The qualities needed by a stage manager include a detailed knowledge of the function of all who contribute towards a production and the ability to carry on undaunted in a crisis. To communicate clearly is vital for any stage manager, who also requires an actor's voice, a scholar's brain and a sense of humour at rehearsal each day, together with the script, pencils and the paraphernalia of the stage manager's table.

The stage manager must be, more or less, nursemaid, confessor, caterer, librarian, stationer, mechanic, actor, mediator, judge, clairvoyant, historian, carpenter chauffeur and linguist – all rolled into one! Any required skill not possessed, any unanswered question, in short any demand or request at all, should be met with total confidence and flair!

Actors will arrive late with nowhere to park, can sometimes damage themselves (and others), get hungry, drunk, sick, electrocuted or depressed, and it is up to the stage management to get them on stage right on cue!

The stage manager must continually monitor the progress of a production for weakness or failure, and know how to keep the process moving ahead towards that immovable deadline – the opening night.

Stages in preparation of a theatre production

The first element is the choice of play – and brings with it the initial management job – securing copies of the text – for both the stage manager and the team, which usually comprises a deputy (DSM) and one or more assistants (ASMs) – then possibly having these available for auditions, which are often managed by a stage manager in a rehearsal room or in the case of a resident company in the actual theatre. Careful planning by the stage manager can make sure these run smoothly, and it offers the first meeting with the director.

Communication being a foundation of the skill of stage management: checking actors' contact details is vital, and will ensure that when bidden "don't call us – we'll call you" – someone does! Several actors auditioning will be cast in the show, and form part of the 'company' whose wellbeing will be your concern for several weeks.

Preliminaries and show preparation

The size of the stage management team will depend on the scale of the production but there will usually be a minimum of three, and this is the moment to start a contact list with details of all the 'creative team' including director, designers responsible for scenery, costumes (if not the same as the set designer), sound, lighting and increasingly important in this modern world – digital video!

Other specialists in that team may include choreography, movement, speech, voice and dialect and sometimes researchers or others needed to share their experience. Don't forget the creators too – author – if living! adapter/translator, musical composer, arranger/orchestrator and so on.

Then come details of those in the making departments. These skills come under the production manager whose job is best described as overseeing the preparation of all the physical assets of the show, tangible and intangible, in contrast to the stage manager who sees to the development of the text in rehearsal with the director and will subsequently run the technical rehearsals and performances.

Making departments, whether in house in a resident company with its own workshops and studios, or contractors, or freelancers, include scenery, props and furniture, lighting, costume, wigs, sound and music, video and armoury if any.

Then detail those responsible for the equivalent running departments, who may well be different, and stage technical departments.

Then there are management positions who will need to be kept informed, often including press, marketing, box office, theatre manager and finance.

Deadlines

If the producing management or the production manager doesn't produce a schedule with significant dates, the stage manager should assemble one. Calculate back from the first performance, whether this is a preview, or press night, allowing time for the production period, embracing technical rehearsals, dress rehearsals and before that the agreed number of ordinary rehearsals before reaching the stage. Computer software spread sheets such as Microsoft Excel often used for calculations is a great way to plan a schedule, and is easily updated.

It is important for the stage manager to be involved in all aspects of the production and to attend as many early discussions with the creative team as possible. Only by being accepted by them from the very beginning can the stage manager build up the firm foundation of a working relationship which will stand for the weeks up to opening.

The Production Meeting

Once all the design proposals have been agreed and there is a scale model and plan and section drawings of the set on the actual stage, the stage manager should call a production meeting with all those suggested above. Proposing date for this early on can help everyone plan their diaries and help to get a full house!

This is an important chance for the director and designer to present their work and discuss the production, and get all enthused about the project. Everyone present should be able to contribute and check what is required of them, including agreeing the budget for all the physical items needed to be made by the production manager's team of makers.

The model should be shown at its best, with small model lights in a darkish room.

Rehearsals

The rehearsal space should be large enough for the whole acting area to be represented, with enough room for the actors to enter end exit to the side, together with free space in front for the director to pace up and down! Further room for tables for the stage manager and other members of the team to visit from time to time is essential and space behind this for discreet comings and goings is needed. In all, a good formula for the over all depth of the room is to have at least half as much again as the acting area.

It is really good if the stage manager can be involved in the choice of the rehearsal room, as they will be the best judge of the needs of the cast and particularly the director who will sometimes have a real aversion to a space. It's too late if they object to the room on the first day of rehearsal! Other aspects are provision of light, both natural and artificial, and access for physical items including rehearsal properties, furniture, costumes and sometimes rehearsal scenery to represent walls steps and raised levels.

Allow time for the 'markup' where sticky tapes are set out to represent the ground plan in real size, entrances and exits and upper areas.

Access is needed to water for company refreshments which will be part of the SM team's responsibility, though many teams make a modest charge (and sometimes a small profit) for this service!

Rehearsal props representing a full rehearsal prop list taken from a careful reading of the script, together with items detailed by the designer which may be peculiar to the way in which the particular production is being staged.

The SM will usually detail one assistant to be in charge of props, and another will manage costume fittings – it's often tricky to prise actors out of rehearsal – so this is often the first time diplomacy is needed! The deputy will be 'on the book' preparing the prompt script with penciled notes of proposed moments when cues for cast or any department's action will be signaled, together with 'blocking' – shorthand notes of all the cast movements during the action of the play.

Stage management must set an example for punctuality, both amongst their team, to allow time for daily preparation of the rehearsal space, and as an example to the acting company. A draft schedule of the whole rehearsal is sometimes made with the director, and varied or reconfirmed on a daily basis.

Some lucky actors have busy lives often with pre-agreed releases for filming or remaining performances with another company – and this is where the SM's Rehearsal Diary becomes important. It's the place to note plans for rehearsal, and meetings and events which will make some unavailable.

The first rehearsal will usually take the form of a model showing – the first for most of the acting company, followed by a read-through possibly with many members of the whole production team. Agreeing the form for this first day with the director is vital. The latter part of the day may be the chance to share costume designs with each actor.

Documentation by the SM team continues with a daily rehearsal note or report generally sent to the whole production team detailing needs or changes that have sprung from the day's work. Email makes distributing information so much easier than in the past, but include a full distribution list so all may see who has received it!

Production progress meetings are usually weekly, and best held in the rehearsal room outside acting rehearsals, and attended by as many departments as possible or their deputies.

As real props and sometimes unusual costume become available these can be fed into rehearsal.

Preparing to move to the stage

The Stage management team now need to tidy up their paperwork. The SM prepares stage cue running lists, and plan scene changes if any, detailing each running crew member's jobs at any time.

The ASM props their setting lists including personal props brought to the stage by the cast, and set dressing notes. The ASM overseeing costume will work with the costume supervisor noting dressing room setting of costumes and wigs and planning for quick changes to take place in the wings or nearby off stage, while the DSM should tidy up their prompt book with penciled notes of cues for all running departments, proposed during rehearsals together with entrance cues for all the cast. These will be preceded during dress rehearsals and performances by calls to the stage for the acting company, and warning standbys for all other cues. Note the penciled requirement; much will change during the technical rehearsal once the show reaches the stage!

The Production Period

The Stage manager should make a firm contribution to the production schedule, which covers the period from an empty stage, rigging sound, lights, flying and setting the scenery, right through to the opening performance.

The schedule should show starting and finishing times initially for the technical departments, focusing the lighting, setting sound and music cues, video or projection, and scene change rehearsals not involving the cast. The DSM will stay through each separate department's plotting session, checking progress against the draft synopsis and noting cue numbers in the prompt script, which will become bible from which the whole show will be run, cued or 'called'.

The 'Tech'

Moving on to the 'technical dress rehearsal', the whole cast, in costume and wigs, along with the technical departments, slowly and methodically piece together the show. Sometimes referred to as the 'stopping dress', time is allowed for stopping and rerunning sequences until everyone contributing their support for the action by the cast is satisfied, all under the supervision of the director, and the whole process managed by the stage manager! In order to make good use of time, the stage manager may agree with the director to 'top and tail', or cut to cue leaving out dialogue during which no physical technical cues are planned. Sections which present no difficulties to the cast can be omitted, but for others working the show it will be their first run. As a guide, schedule three times the duration of the action. A good technical dress rehearsal with proper attention to detail should prevent physical details worrying the cast. The performer's challenges are exposed to the public. The stage manager is there to reduce these to a minimum.

During the technical dress rehearsal, where possible, the stage manager should sit out front near the director, lighting and sound designers; this will enable them to have a detailed understanding of the shape of the whole show, in preparation for their team running and maintaining the standard of the performances, however many, and in some cases rehearsing understudies, replacing cast members during a long run, or replacement actors for touring.

The Dress Rehearsal

There may be one or more dress rehearsals planned, and these should aim to be straight run-throughs, only stopping for major stoppages perhaps involving scenery.   These provide an opportunity for the director to work on interpretation and acting notes. One of these rehearsals may permit photographs to be taken by the production photographer, even permitting shots taken from on stage amongst the cast! Notice must be given if this is to happen to ensure the costume department provide full clothing and wigs.

Each rehearsal should be followed by note sessions agreed by the stage manager with the director – bearing in mind late working criteria – and involving any or all of the SM team, acting company – if not given separately the next day, running crew heads, technical operators and the creative team. Changes will then be consolidated, cue lists and prompt book updated, ready for the opening.

The old adage of a bad dress rehearsal preceding a good first night is famous. Phrases like "It'll be alright on the night" or a favourite version, "It'll be alright under light"!! may contain a grain of truth, but underlying the tension, excitement and celebration of the first night must run the basic discipline that the stage management firmly intends to prevail for the run of the production, however brief.

Good organisation, thorough preparation and calm attention to detail are important at all stages of a production, but they are particularly vital before the opening night.   Preshow checks are often done with two of the SM team together – including working parts of the set, including doors, props being correctly set both on and off stage, cue lights working, cue sheets, plots and departmental scripts in position, and at the 'half' – 35 minutes before curtain up – that all actors and show technicians are present.

After the performance the SM should prepare a report recording accurate timings of each scene or act and intervals. Variations of even a minute or two on sequences in the show need investigation and are often a sign of something untoward. This should include notes of any variation to the rehearsed action, and any unintentional events or absences.

Well done! The show has opened! Now plan to copy or back up all documentation including the prompt book – too much has been invested to risk loss!

Remind the cast and crew of their next call – and join the first night party!

Jason Barnes

THE STAGE—SETTING THE SCENES.

Working at Heights

The HSE (Health and Safety Executive) has issued guidance on Working at Heights, specifically for the theatre, and the ABTT (Association of British Theatre Technicians) published a Code of Practice 'For the selection and use of temporary access equipment for working at height in theatres' in 2011.

The code of Practice is clearly written and presents a logical guide over more than 100 pages. A copy may be requested from the ABTT by emailing workatheight@abtt.org.uk.

There is a concise HSE Summary

The following, depending on individual circumstances, are examples of reasonably practicable for working at height.

- No work at heights – remote or low level focusing of lights. All scenery, etc completed at ground level and lifted into place.
- Work from existing workplace – existing gantries, walkways, catwalks or trampoline grids.
- Work platforms – mobile towers and MEWPS.
- Work positioning – fixed length wires and harnesses.
- Fall mitigation – airbags/nets etc. Fall protection using inertia reel harnesses or similar. Rescue plan must be in place.
- Other equipment requiring detailed systems of work – Ladders, Zarges, Tallescopes etc.

The common sense and legal key to safe practice is a Risk Assessment carried out by a competent person.

A suitable and sufficient risk is one that:

- Identifies the hazards and those at risk
- Evaluates and prioritises the risks
- Decides on preventative actions
- Takes action
- Records the action
- Monitors and reviews the situation

Table 1.5.1 shows an example risk assessment following an HSE model. Other models are available. Risk assessments are often based on a numerical assessment.

Table 1.5.2 (below) shows the basis for one such assessment.

Table 1.5.2 : Sample risk assessment grading system				
Severity	Likelihood	No. of people affected	Risk Factor	Action
1 = Trivial Injury	1 = Improbable	1 = 1 person	< 4	Acceptable
2 = Minor injury	2 = Unlikely	2 = 1 to 5 people	5 – 10	Low priority
3 = '3 day' injury	3 = Possible	3 = 6 to 10 people	11 – 14	Medium priority
4 = Major injury	4 = Likely	4 = 11– 50 people	15 – 20	High priority
5 = Death	5 = Probable	= > 50 people	>20	Urgent priority

The revised Code of Practice does include a section on the revised modifications for the use of Tallescopes.

Four push-pull posts B so operators do not have to bend at the waist and can steer more easily and with a better view.

Four non-lifts castors fitted so not to cause any movements in the Tallescope when brakes are being engaged or disengaged. The brakes should be applied when the Tallescope is not in motion.

Four outriggers reduce the possibility of a Tallescope falling sideways. The outriggers are locked off with the feet not more than 10mm above the floor.

Tom Gibberd (left) and Mike Christophi (right) demonstrate the "three fours" at the ATG Waterside Theatre in Aylesbury

The Stage Tool Cupboard

So much can be told about the way a stage is run simply by opening up the Stage Cupboard. Is it devoid of tools except maybe broken down staple gun with the wrong size staples, or is it a treasure trove of useful gizmos to make the production run smoothly? A joy to behold!

Everyone would have their own idea of the perfect stage cupboard and the way it is organised would reflect the colourful character of those who work on the stage.

Here is a suggestion. The cupboard should be of stout wooden construction which is lockable at the end of each day. Try to find a position in the corner of the stage so everything is to hand. A wooden cupboard allows screw eyes, cup hooks and brackets to be fixed easily. Alternatively a shadow board could be used but it will need someone to police it to ensure the tools are returned.

Keep a coloured aerosol spray and some coloured tapes to mark all the theatre's tools distinctly in an unusual colour. Tools are often inadvertently taken by touring companies genuinely thinking the tool belongs to them. There is no excuse if they are all sprayed or taped in an unusual colour!

Measuring and Marking

Stage Tape – needs to be long enough to stretch right across your stage. Glass Fibre tapes are best as they will survive being stood on. Choose one with a nice comfortable winding handle.

Tape Measure – about 8m is perfect for the average stage. Try to get one with a good 'stand out' for measuring up to the tops of the scenery. If you are going to wear the tape on your belt don't forget to consider how bulky and heavy the tape will be – choose one that is just long enough.

Chalk Line – essential for marking out the 'Setting Line' and 'Centreline' on the stage. Some Chalk Lines are usefully geared for fast retrieval. Keep a good stock of different coloured chalks too.

Trammel Heads – are useful for marking out revolving or circular stages and pivoting trucks. They just clamp to any piece of wood long enough to form the radius. A makeshift arrangement can easily be made with two nails and a length of timber.

Combination Square – this is the most useful type of square with a built in spirit level and 45 degree face. The rule can be fixed off at different positions so the square can also be used as a Marking Gauge.

Roofing Square – a big steel square generally 600 x 410mm that is great for marking out sheets of plywood. Good ones will have "Rafter Tables" on them which conveniently show the correct positions for marking out corner braces.

Spirit Levels – are normally supplied as long 'Girder Levels' or short 'Torpedo' levels. The long girder level is probably the best choice for the stage cupboard as it perfect for setting up most scenery. The short 'Torpedo' levels can, however, be carried on your belt and are magnetic so they are great for setting up steel scaffolding.

Traditional Brass Plumb Bobs – are useful for 'spotting blocks' (positioning pulleys) in the theatre grid. Nowadays Laser Plumb Bobs are popular as many can self-level giving quick and accurate results. Of course you may prefer to improvise with any weight on a piece of string. If you have a transparent bucket try putting the bob into the water, it will settle down to its final position much more quickly.

Bashing and Trashing

Claw Hammer – This need not be anything special, just a traditional claw hammer with a wood or fibreglass handle. About 16oz would be ideal. With the popularity of cordless drill/drivers, nails are used less and less nowadays but they can still provide a quick and strong method of construction especially when used in a dovetail fashion with a good PVA adhesive.

Magnetic Tack Hammer – Some theatres tack out canvas floor cloths onto their stage. These magnetic head hammers are ideal for this task. Generally 7oz **Tacklifter** – useful for lifting small tacks and nails

Copper Rawhide Hammer – The rawhide face is good for working with aluminium truss. Normally they weigh just over 1kg.

Paviours Maul – These large rubber headed mauls are perfect for shunting rostra, and heavy scenery into place without causing the damage associated with using stage weights. Not essential but highly recommended.

Crow Bars – These are useful for stripping out old nails from timber and for raising heavy pieces of scenery into final position prior to being bolted into place. There are many different types including large bars with rollers for moving scenery into place and small Japanese style bars which will be ideal for removing mouldings and stubborn screws.

Sawing and Cutting

Panel Saw – Any 'hard point' saw about 20" long will be fine. These saws do not require sharpening and are economical to purchase. Many have a straight back and special handle so they can also be used as squares.

Hacksaw – Unless you are expecting major alterations any economical 12" hacksaw should suffice but it is well worth investing in bi-metal unbreakable blades which are much safer especially if you are working overhead.

A Tube Cutter – can be handy for cutting down conduit pipes and scaffolding tube. They are quiet in operation so a bit of sneaky work can take place during the technical rehearsals without disturbing everyone. Ones fitted with bearings cut more easily.

Tube Reamers – will quickly remove any sharp shards of steel from recently cut scaffold or conduit helping to avoid nasty cut fingers or, worse still, torn cloths.

Stanley Knife – is still very popular but there are also a wide variety of other knives available which take standard craft blades. Retractable or folding versions are safer but if you are using fixed blade versions them make sure you have a belt scabbard – putting them in your pocket is not a good idea!

You will need a good stock of craft blades. It is most economical to buy a box of these – sharp blades are safer than blunt ones. Also consider a pack of serrated craft blades which cut through rope easily and some unbreakable blades for working at height.

Wire Cutters – Choose a pair of cutters one size up from the normal cable you will cut. Cutters are hard work when cutting the maximum specified wire size but slice easily through the smaller sizes.

Shears – You will need good pair of large scissors that will cut easily through canvas.

Woodworking

Block Plane – A little block plane is very useful for removing the arris from timber to prevent splinters. The real classic is the Stanley 9½ model but many cheaper versions exist.

Chisels – 12mm, 18mm and 25mm wide chisels will cover most uses. Try to buy ones with unbreakable handles or you will need to buy a wooden mallet too (and make sure the stage staff use it!)

Oilstone – You will need one of these. Either choose a diamond stone or a traditional oilstone. A honing guide is a very useful addition and you will need a wooden box too.

Fixing and Fastening

Podgers – These tools have a long pointed shaft to align bolt holes and a ratchet head on the other end to tighten up the nuts. The 17/19 mm version will fit M10 and M12 bolts and is the most popular size. Four-way versions are also available fitting M10, M12, 7/16" scaffolding and M24 truss fittings. Two or ideally four would be ideal.

Quad Spanner – A useful and popular type of ratchet spanner that will fit M8, M10, M12 and most scaffolding.

Adjustable Spanner – The trusty AJ will always get you out of trouble. 8" is the best size and it's good to have two of them.

Wing Bolt Spanner – This tool will get those tight wing nuts on hook clamps loosened off.

Socket Set – A good socket set will always be appreciated and sometimes a ratchet handle with an extension will be the only way to access some nuts. If you have an impact driver then consider an impact socket set.

Set of screwdrivers – It is best to choose the kind of screwdriver that can withstand some abuse. The ones with the steel going right through the handle and have a hex section to take a spanner are perfect. Tough and corroded screws can be assisted with a whack and they can be safely abused as levers, etc.

Nut Spinners – 7mm nut spinners will fit the small nuts on 3-4mm cable grips which are often encountered. They are much faster than using adjustable spanners.

Allen Keys – You will need a 6mm and an 8mm for key clamps but a fold out set including those sizes would be better and harder to loose.

Staple Guns – A good quality steel bodied gun is generally the best but be careful not to get one which is too heavy.

Wire Staples – are easy to fire and less tiring whereas the flat wire staple guns tend to have tougher springs which can be tiring on the hand. Hammer tackers are not so popular nowadays but they are still the fastest and easiest way to canvas a flat without using air powered tools.

Staple Remover – A handy small tool that will easily remove staples.

Squeezing Things!

One Handed Clamps – These economical clamps are handy for general woodworking as well as holding scenery together.

Try to buy black ones. At least four would be needed but the more the merrier.

G Clamps – A few 6" G Clamps are handy for heavier work. At least two would be needed.

Long Clamps – A couple of long clamps will always be handy. The longest clamps are generally sold as clamp heads which slide along steel tube or timber. Sash clamps generally come in 36" or 48" lengths or T bar clamps come up to 78". A pair would be needed. Sash clamps generally come in 36" or 48" lengths or T bar clamps come up to 78". A pair would be needed.

Vice Grip Pliers – These locking grip pliers are particularly useful as a spare set of hands when working by yourself. 175mm is a useful size.

Combination Pliers – A handy tool with wire cutting blades. Many stage staff will already carry a Multitool with pliers on them.

Power Tools

Extension Leads – Simple leads with tough rubber sockets are often better than reels, especially if you are working up a ladder. Why not buy a 100m drum of cable and make up your own? Make sure they have a home.

Mains Percusion Drill – A mains drill still has its uses. It should be able to happily drill 13mm holes in steel and have a percussion feature for drilling into brick.

Mains Jig Saw – Essential for cutting curves but they will also cut a reasonable straight line if no circular saw is available.

Circular Saw – Larger stages could find this to be a useful tool. The types supplied with long guide rails are best.

Angle Grinder – These will get you out of trouble if some steel scenery doesn't quite fit. A 115mm version is very popular but the 230mm version will tackle bigger cutting tasks.

Cordless Tools – In the ideal world each stage crew would have their own small 10.8V cordless drill and impact driver which would be their personal kit. If you are going to buy cordless tools for the Stage Cupboard then consider the following:

    a. Best to go for lithium ion batteries, they are lighter and last longer.
    b. Try to choose one manufacturer so that the batteries and chargers are interchangeable.
    c. If the batteries will not interchange between tool at least check to see if one charger will charge all the voltages.
    d. Consider buying 'bare units' to dramatically reduce costs and just interchange the batteries.

Stage House Keeping Gear

Brooms – Every stage should have at least one wide Gumati bristle broom (36") and one small (12") one for each side of the stage with dedicated storage clips or wall brackets.

Magnetic Sweeper – If you are using carpet tacks for you stage cloths and have ballet performances then a magnetic sweeper is a useful bit of kit!

Dustpan and brush – Strong wide opening pan with a fairly stiff brush for general tidying.

Roller and Tray – After the show has been struck it is good to be able to freshen up the black paintwork with a quick roll over. A 9" medium pile roller and long handle make quick work of this task.

Alasdair Flint

The National Theatre Paint Frame 2007

A Short Guide to Scene Painting for Schools and Amateurs

Scene painting is about communicating a visual message and the art is understanding the techniques by which enlarged images may clearly inform the audience's eye. The visual scene must always support the production. At its best, it will inform and delight but never distract nor be self-indulgent.

The large scale of scenic art for flattage or scenic canvas can be daunting, and it's a good idea to make a scaled drawing divided into a grid of equal squares, with some ideas of colours. A scale of 1:25 or ½" to the foot is preferred.

Preparing to paint

The scenery, either flat on a floor (with a plastic sheet laid down to protect the floor finish) or hung vertically; is divided up into squares in the same way as the gridded design. The outlines are drawn in chalk or charcoal, which can be corrected or changed easily. When plotted, stand back, look, and adjust before starting to paint.

Priming

A canvas or flattage needs a priming coat, as canvas, or raw wood soaks up paint too quickly. Rosco's Flexbond is a commercial example – a PVA glue to seal a canvas weave before painting – diluted 1:4 or 1:6 with water. A prime needs to be flexible and it may be tinted with water-based paints.

Priming colour

Generally an off-white or neutral colour is preferred to pure white, unless colours need a white background to give brilliance to their hue.

To re-use scenery, an obliterating coat of preferred colours should be applied first.

Paint supplies

Paints for theatrical work should always be water-based to retain the non-flammability of the scenery. Specialist paints are made for scenic artists, notably Rosco, Bristol and Winsor Newton. Ranges of special glazes, fluorescent and phosphorescent paints are available.

Textures

Plain flat surface colours are often called for by the set designer, or lighting designer, so be careful with household emulsions which have a slight sheen.

Extra 'life' can be given, by mixing a slightly lighter or darker tone of the base colour and then spatter, spray, stipple or sponge over – it will 'vibrate'.

Everything in life has texture; it can be achieved for scenery by two or more overlaid colours, dragging a brush load of contrasting colours to simulate wood grains or spattering to give a pebbly effect, or sponging to create stonework.

Tools of the trade

You must use good brushes, to retain shape during use, and of a long length which holds more paint. 6" or 7" brushes are best for large areas and prinning, and a range of ½ ", 1", 2", 3" or even 4" are good for detail work.

Brushes are the best way to achieve straight ruled lines, there are bristle lining brushes in a wide range of sizes.

Spray painting

Using a spray gun is a skill that needs to be practised, and there are four golden rules:

Always strain the paint

Never have the air pressure higher than needed to atomise the paint

Wear a face mask

Clean the equipment immediately after use

Cut rollers for texture and pattern

Cut rollers are a quick and easy method to produce texture. Use 7" foam rollers to cut and tear them to create knobbly effects for stonework or foliage. Mark regular incisions to paint parallel lines – wood grain, weave or engraving effects.

Large patterns can be made from stencils or foam rubber stamps. For stencils, buy sheets of oiled manila from an art shop and use a sharp knife to cut out your pattern – good for wallpaper, brick, parquet or tile effects.

Deeper foam makes it more pressure sensitive. Experimentation is the key.

Enjoy

Above all, the act of scene painting should be enjoyed – it is a creative process, translating the idea or image from the designer to something on a big scale for the stage: artistic and satisfying.

Chris Clark

Mr Joseph Harker on the New Drury Lane scenery, 15th April 1922.

Painting a Backcloth for Alice in Wonderland

This backcloth was painted for Christopher Wheeldon's ballet *Alice's Adventures in Wonderland*, performed by the Royal Ballet at the Royal Opera House in 2011, for the scene in which the caterpillar smokes a hookah sitting in a mushroom.

The Designer Bob Crowley's idea was that Chris Clark's cloth should evoke a smokey atmosphere of mushrooms with long wavy stalks, to be displayed through a hazy gauze.

The 'mushrooms' imaginatively became maharajah's parasols and the whole scene had an Eastern flavour, including the choreography and music.

In front of it all, there was a real ' practical' mushroom for the Caterpillar to do his act, and it would be decorated in Indian Style embroidery and lush blue fabrics to match.

Chris and Liz were left to develop the design in their paint studio and the designer was pleased with their development of the concept of his ideas and references.

The cloth was painted in Rosco Ultramarine Blue and the darks produced by adding purples and Prussian Blue, never black.

They made half templates, based on the real prop mushroom, to reproduce the six different sizes of parasol mushroom motifs, embroidery effects in blue and silver.

This is a good example of true collaboration between the director, designer and scenic artists.

Chris and Liz Clark

Theatrical Fog

Fog or haze is often called for in productions and fog and haze machines are widely available from distributors for sale or hire, along with their proprietary fog fluids.

FOG is a thick white opaque atmospheric effect that lasts a short while and HAZE is a lighter more translucent, mist like effect, and tends to hang longer.

The fog effect is created because when light hits a fog droplet it scatters the light in all directions. The purpose of fog or haze is to create a special effect of atmospheric enhancement, or with haze, to make light beams visible.

The safest and easiest way to produce fog or haze, is to use a fog or haze machine, made by a member, or distributed by a member of PLASA (see entry on PLASA p199) and their fog fluid.

Fog machines heat the fog fluid and pump it, under pressure, into the atmosphere as an aerosol of fog droplets.

Fog machine control can be on a timer or by direct manual control, or by DMX. The proprietary fluid is a special mixture of glycol fluids and deionised water.

PLASA have a 55 page document on fog use, and we quote abbreviated basic Guidelines for use of fog on stage.

Basic Fog Use Guidelines

- Determine the appropriate technology for the application
- Make only as much fog as necessary
- Deliver fog only where necessary
- Deliver fog only when it is necessary
- Avoid exposing people to the direct output of fog machines
- Monitor and control liquid accumulation
- Post appropriate warnings
- Follow manufacturers' instructions

Some Information on Use and Frequently Asked Questions

Can you colour fog?

No, do not ever add anything to the manufacturers' fluid. The best way to colour fog is to use coloured light projected on it.

Can you have different flavours?

Yes, check the manufacturer of fluid; some market scented fluids. Do not add anything yourself. (DJ's have been known to add after-shave!)

Can you have fast moving fog, say, for the barricades of Les Miserables?

Yes, place a floor mounted fan in front of the machine.

Can you have low lying fog like dry ice?

Yes – dry ice is available commercially, but must be used carefully, observing health and safety guide-lines. Remember dry ice is a solid

Top: theatrical fog, bottom: low fog, photos: Rosco.

form of carbon dioxide. There was a show where the low lying dry ice 'fog' dropped – because it's heavy – into the orchestra pit. As a result the music stopped, as there was too little oxygen around for the players. The best way is to cool conventional fog by passing it over ice, or use the fog machine manufacturer's product for this.

Can you pipe or duct fog?

Yes – Use a special attachment for the machine and use a 4" diameter flexible hose, which can be pieced at the required intervals.

How safe is fog?

Follow the manufacturers' guidelines; avoid anyone being subjected to fog at close range from the machine. Stage managers should check that no fluid drips onto the floor under the machine exist nozzle, as this can make it slippery.

Conflagration as seen inside the Castle.

Stage Make up

Stage Make up is both a science and an art. It is designed to help make the performer believable to the audience to enhance the character charisma on stage.

Stage make up can be challenging, it may look exaggerated in close up, but be natural to the audience, and to be seen under stage lighting.

Some essential points are:

- Good permanence on the actor's skin for the whole performance.
- Especially good compatibility on the skin.
- Good colour intensity.
- High degree of product safety and reliability.

Remember that with stage lights and a strenuous action on stage, makeup must withstand perspiration: audiences tend to dislike actors streaming with sweat – shine can be minimised using waterproof elements, cream foundation, rouges and eye colour last longer than powder.

Use professional stage make up created for the purpose. Popular brands include: Ben Nye, Max Factor, Mehron, Kryolan and Grimas.

To Work

- For small groups, schools and amateurs, you are generally expected to do your own make up.
- The 'look' may be decided by the director or the 'design' by a make up artist, but you have to create it, skilfully, for a consistency for the character in performance.

Here's How

- Wash your face carefully with warm or hot water and take care to exfoliate and rinse with cold water to close the pores.
- Follow with a toner and moisturise to create a clean smooth base for the make up.
- Apply a concealer for any uneven colour areas of your skin.
- Use a foundation brush or sponge to apply the foundation for very even coverage.
- The foundation – best a high quality cream a few shades lighter or darker than your natural skintone. It does not need to be heavy if in a small theatre or performance space.
- If you have a naturally dark skintone, Indian, Asian, African, Afro-Caribbean, try and match a good base colour and use a finishing powder.

- Theatre lighting may wash out features of an actor's face; stage make up and technique can change this.
- 'Contour' areas that protrude, like nose and cheekbones should be highlighted with a lighter colour, and areas that recede, like eye sockets or the sides of the nose should be darker.
- Reduce plumpness and strengthen your jawline by adding colour as a subtle shadow line from the chin to the lower edge of your jaw.
- For eyebrows, use an eyebrow pencil to darken eyebrows and create a high arch, a good arch frames the face. For dramatic roles use thick black lines. For men and younger performers use brown.
- To open up the eyes and widen them use pale cream colours for highlights to the centre of the lids and brow bones.
- Make sure to blend colour into the hair line and that the jawline colour blends into the neck.
- Line the mouth with a firm dark line that enhances the natural mouth shape.
- Stage make up is not life – it's meant to emphasise features under stage lighting and to be seen from afar.
- To finish, powder the entire face thoroughly.
- Get feedback from the director and lighting designer and from house level in rehearsal, and tweak if necessary.
- Remove make up after the show however tired you are: use cream or oil based make up removers on the eyes and a good face cleaner.
- Finally tools of the trade: one brush does not suit all; there are good selections on the market, for instance Chas Fox and Grimas.
- Don't be in a rush to buy a big palette of colour, small palettes are available, for instance from Kryolan.

Insight from a Professional

The great Marlene Dietrich was a renowned beauty of the 1920s onward, on stage and film.

She always insisted on a single high key light and she preferred to be lit on stage by one favoured lighting designer – Joe Davis – one of the founding fathers of lighting design skills. He even lit her for a private function at Buckingham Palace.

She painted a blue line down the middle of her nose to minimise its tilt, and never wanted to be seen in profile, then painted a white line on the inside of her eyelids to emphasise the key light reflection.

Do not try this at home!

Greasepaint

A term to encompass all forms of stage make up. Leichners used to make sticks of Greasepaint to apply over a base and No 5 and 9 were used to create a flesh colour, with males using more 9 than females. After the War, Max Factor introduced a range of make up creams, which proved very popular. All performers applied their own make up and 'Make up Artists' were not used at all. I worked with Jimmy 'that's yer lot' Wheeler who I saw apply his make up once. He opened his violin case, took out a candle and a cork from a wine bottle, lit the candle, blackened the end of the cork in the candle flame, and put two strokes under his nose, to represent his trademark moustache, and all done in two minutes! "Right, boy, where do you want me?" he said as we walked out of the dressing room!

Ham Actors

An early form of greasepaint make up was made from a base of ham fat. Thus a second rate artist who used too much, was known as a 'ham actor' and was known to 'ham it up a bit'.

John Toogood *(extract from Greasepaint and Ham Actors)*

Edge-Safe for Stage Edge Safety

Edge-Safe was launched at the ABTT Theatre Show in June 2011 and won the ABTT's 'Widget Product of the Year' award for the best new theatre product of 2011. It improves safety working on and off the stage.

Edge-Safe is a ribbed ramp of heavy synthetic rubber that is designed to be mounted along the front edge of a stage. The manufacturers recommend attaching it to the stage edge, but each unit is heavy enough to offer protection even if not fixed down, whilst being light enough to be repositioned or stored easily. Edge-Safe is so tough it can stop flight cases, Tallescopes or other wheeled equipment rolling over the stage edge. Not only will it make the stage area safer during fit up, it'll allow crew to work more quickly and effectively. Angled so it is easily viewed from on stage, it indicates the stage edge with a reflective strip that is visible to crew and performers in all light conditions (perfect for performers in dark scenes or if they are being dazzled by spotlights). Just 5cm high it has a vertical matt black edge to the front so is virtually invisible to the audience.

Traditional Theatre Jargon

Extracts from Traditional Theatre /Jargon/Definitions/Quotes/ etc which were once in everyday use by the Theatre People

Bouncing the Tabs

When taking curtain calls, it is traditional for the house tabs to be 'bounced' in and out. The stage management instructs the head flyman "On the bounce, please" for all calls prior to the final call, which was always 'hand-over-hand', i.e. slowly.

Clacker A 'plant' in the audience to encourage laughter, clapping and general audience participation. Often used by a comic to have his routine received better.

Digs Theatrical rooms for touring artists, posted out by the stage-door keeper, giving details of local boarding houses used to 'theatricals' staying. Some provided a meal or sandwiches with a bottle of beer for a post-show supper, and did not disturb guests until after mid-day. Other indicated that the rate charged included 'use of cruet' as an added attraction.

Dips Were a small trap, set into the stage floor, where one could plug in a piece of electrical equipment to be operated via the main switchboard.

Deck A term for the stage floor, that dates back to when traditionally sailors worked backstage, because of their knowledge of knots etc.

Dry Ice Blocks or pieces of frozen carbon dioxide when immersed in hot water produce the effect of fog. This 'gas' sits low on the stage floor, and drifts downstage on the rake, and is a danger to health if inhaled. It is essential when using dry ice in pantomime, to ensure that you have access to, or hire a container, to store the blocks/bags in, and that it is large enough to accommodate all that will be required over the festive season, as ICI who produce it, traditionally close down for a long Christmas break each year.

Firearms Safe

A safe large enough to lock away any firearms which are to be used in the show, when not in use. The 'bolts' and blanks should be stored in a separate lockable container/safe. The firearms should be set out in the wings at the last possible time, as it has been known for a firearm to be 'borrowed' and used in a spate of robberies. There was an occasion when police suddenly realised that the local robberies were all being carried out on the same day, at the same time each week – the matinee day!

Fish and Actors

Observation made by British Railways staff when they saw a carriage and a truck in a siding on a Sunday. A 'fish and chip' tour was a tour that was contracted to play the smallest theatres. It was also known as 'The Woolworth Circuit' named after the cheap high street store. Railway privileges enabled touring companies to free scenery trucks, dependent on the number of tickets bought for artists. For companies between 20-33 artists they were permitted one free scenery truck not exceeding 21 feet in length. For Companies with 167-200 passengers, six scenery trucks were free of charge. To comply with these regulations, it was not unknown for the company manager to buy 'extra' tickets, for non existent members of the company.

Ghost on Friday

Was a theatrical term, between actors to inquire if the manager had been round to pay them yet. Now more usually used as 'the ghost walks to-day' or 'when does the ghost walk?' meaning what day do we get paid? The 'treasury call' was usually at noon on a Friday, but of late, has been held on a Thursday in the 'treasury room' as at TRDL, or the company office. In the days of vaudeville and variety 'the ghost walked' during the second house of the final performance, to ensure that no act 'skipped' away without doing the final performance. It was also done then, as the company manager would be in possession of his take of the box office receipts, for that week, after Contra deductions.

Kabuki A term from the theatre of Japan, that means 'a sudden, dramatic, revelation or transformation'. It was used in British theatre by hanging a cloth or drape, which was required to fall down to the deck on cue, by locating reinforced eyelets along the top of the cloth and then placing them over pegs set into a round wooded batten. They could be flown in/out as normal till required to fall. On cue the round batten was rotated 180 degrees, and the cloth fell from the pegs.

Key to the Grid

A junior member of staff would be sent to the manager's office to ask for the 'key for the grid'. After a long delay, and lots of searching, the manager would send the junior member of staff back to his HoD to inform them that the key could not be found or was lost, and that it would be necessary to break into the grid! The joke was complete, and you felt such a fool for falling for it!

Left Shoe

It is a superstition in the theatre for an artist to put on and take off the left shoe first. Its origins are unknown, but they do it!

Letterbox

A term used when plotting a 'limes/followspot' cue for the shape to be in a letterbox shape (used particularly when a whole company takes its call.) A 'Postbox' shape was tall and narrow at the base and top.

Loading Gallery

A narrow platform above the fly gallery where the counterweights are stored, and are loaded/unloaded into the counterweight cradles to balance the item to be flown.

Limes A name derived from an early form of followspots that produced 'limelight'. This was produced by directing a jet of burning gas (oxyhydrogen) over a cylinder of lime (calcium carbonate). In later days, two carbon rods were primed before use, and slowly fed against each other, leaving a small gap between the two, which the DC current would 'arc' between, to produce an intense white light. One of the most respected operators of the 'followspot' is Linford Hudson, who was in the 'limes box' for 50 years at The London Palladium.

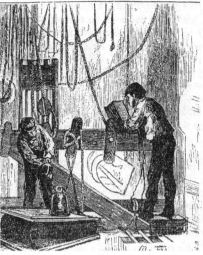

Lime-light men operating in the fly-gallery.
***The Graphic**, 3 Jan. 1874, p. 1.*

Oranges

Oranges are not welcome backstage because of its pungent smell, and the problem of the juice squirting into someone's eyes. It has not been unknown for an understudy to deliberately squirt orange juice (by accident?) in the eye of the person that they are covering, in order to get on by any means, fair or foul.

Ostrich Feathers

It is considered lucky to have ostrich feathers on-stage because of the 'evil eye' on them.

Paint Frame

A frame in a scenic workshop with enough height to hang a cloth and full drop. The scenic artist could hen work on the cloth by moving the frame up or down to the level where he was working. Flats could also be painted in this way by nailing the flats upright onto the battens of the frame.

Periaktoi

Is a term first used in Greek Theatre, for a boat truck with scenery set on it in a triangular shape, so that it can be turned to display three different scenes. Sometimes the flats on the boat truck were changed at the interval, to give more options.

Piano When setting a grand piano (baby or concert) on stage for an artist, it should be set with the keyboard end facing stage right. The piano lid can then be lifted to 'bounce' the sound downstage, and make it more audible.

Quotes "Actor's a guy who, if you ain't talking about him, he ain't listening" (*Marlon Brando*).

"Acting is merely the art of keeping a large group of people from coughing" (*Ralf Richardson*).

"The play was a great success, but the audience was a disaster" (*Oscar Wilde*).

"I used to be a 'Tour-de de Force', but now am forced to tour!" (*Sybil Thorndike*).

Swag   A term used mainly in variety shows, for the 'looping up' of drapes to create an attractive stage setting for the artist to perform in. By sewing metal rings about the size of a 10p, onto the back of a drape, one could vary the shape created by pulling the cord, passing through the rings, and several resident stage managers were well noted for their expertise in this field.

Tabs   The day to day word for 'the tableau curtain'. When hanging a set of house tabs, (with a break in the middle) it is the correct procedure for the stage right half to be hung on the same bar as the stage left half but slightly behind it, with an overlap of about three feet at the centre. It is hung this way to enable the prompt corner to see when the tabs are being paged open to enable an artist, (mainly in opera and ballet) to step through the opening to take a solo call, and receive a bouquet from the 'flunkly' in powered wig and breeches. The act drop (a Victorian stretched painted canvas) when dropped in, indicated that there was more to come. The house tabs indicated that it is the end. The last surviving original act drop is in the Gaiety Theatre on the Isle of Man, and in 1996 a reproduction of one was hung in Her Majesty's Theatre, in Ballarat, Australia.

John Toogood

Extracts from *Theatre Lore* by Nick Bromley

Actor Manager

Is now that rare species of a performer – an actor prepared to produce plays and therefore one who not only gets to play all the best parts but pays others to play the worst.

Actor Proof

A part so brilliantly written that not even the worst actor in the world (see awards) can ruin or destroy it. This, of course, is a perfect example of a theatrical myth.

Advance Bars

One needs balls of steel and grim determination to make it to advance bars. These are positioned high above the auditorium just in front of the proscenium arch and are used to hang lanterns and speakers. Please don't be tempted to swing on them no matter what their load bearing is.

Their supporting cables pass through holes in the plastered ceiling and this plaster is generally as old as the theatre. It doesn't like its routine disturbed and like an elderly relative is inclined to suddenly drop off and upset the inheritance of those working below.

Artiste   Not the genteel way of spelling the word, or for that matter a misspelling but the correct if antiquated way of describing a performer in the world of variety. It made them sound posh even if their landladies knew better.

Backing Flat (a)

A small piece of painted scenery often used with interior sets. It is placed, for example, behind an on-stage entrance so that the audience can believe the illusion that the doorway leads into a sumptuous corridor.

This belief is maintained until the unbraced backing flat topples over, the door opens and the reality of a sordid wing is revealed.

Border Refers to neither Break for the Border, a long gone, watering-hole located in the depths of the Palladium cellars, nor a singular short-lived bookshop but a simple piece of dusty black tat. This can be of varying length and if stretched horizontally in the air from one side of the sage to the other will conceal from the audience all sorts of things which hang from grid e.g. lights, scenery, flymen, etc, etc…

Designer (four types of)

You will meet four categories of designers in the Theatre:

Set designer, Lighting designer, Sound designer, Costume designer

Quite often the set designer doubles up as the costume designer and that's why in some shows you can't tell the difference between the curtains and the costumes.

However it's a theatrical truth that all four categories, with the very odd exception, are brim full of lovely people who understand instinctively the difficulties their designs bring to everybody else. It's a measure of their artistic integrity that they don't give a damn.

Iron (the)

Not to be confused with that fine actor Jeremy, who is, of course, plural.

The Iron is a theatre's fire curtain which resides for most of a show above the proscenium opening. It straddles the whole and when lowered completely blocks out an audience or performance. This can be very useful on more riotous productions.

Irons do have a tendency to creep in so it's advisable to keep your actors and yourself always upstage of them.

Mattress

Not to be confused with Mistress.

Mattresses will come in useful if you are doing such plays as Les Liasons Dangereuses even if they are a bit grubby by the end of the run. They are also very good for breaking people's falls after a dramatic onstage exit.

If the soprano's really pissing you off you can soften Tosca's fall from the heights of Castel Sant'Angelo by substituting a trampoline for a mattress, but make sure it's the final performance.

Mirror Curtain

Not for ageing chorines to admire their merkins but a unique front curtain constructed in 1822 for the Royal Coburg Theatre, or, as it is known now,

The Old Vic.

The Royal Coburg had been built in the belief that it would attract genteel audience from north of the river, but the area around Waterloo was, if you can believe this, even rougher then than it is today. The curtain was constructed of 66 pieces of glass. It was meant to be an irresistible novelty but it only succeeded in scaring the rowdy crowd out of their wits by giving them for once a candid view of themselves.

All efforts to lift it then failed, and the show was cancelled until it had been dismantled. Safe from further self-discovery, the mob returned to earn the theatre the reputation of a blood bucket.

Even Edmund Kean, no prude himself – his contractual requirements specified two bottles of brandy and three whores per interval – found them rough going.

At the end of a hard week in 1831 he told his last audience that: "In my life I have never acted to such a set of ignorant, unmitigated brutes as I have before me."

His successors today have unknowingly never had it so good.

Mister Jet*

When someone in the know sidles up to you in the wing and whispers hoarsely in your ear that Mr Jet's in the building, they are not suggesting that you phone the Sun hotline and rush around to the box office to find what seat he's in. They're telling you the code words that mean there's a fire and, however small it may be, that's serious, very, very serious.

Fire is rightly considered the theatre's Enemy No 1 by local authority officials, for they, unlike producers, have no trivial reason to fear the critics or the attractions of artistic entertainment such as Strictly Come Dancing or Tate Modern.

Fire is an ancient enemy that has consumed theatres for centuries.

Famous London victims of its savagery include Shakespeare's Globe in

The fire at the New Theatre Royal, Exeter, 5th September, 1887.
From The Illustrated London News, vol.91, 10th September, 1887.

1613 and the Theatre Royal Drury Lane, twice torched in 1672 and 1809. The second conflagration may have destroyed the whole building despite its iron curtain, but, in compensation, it afforded its owner Richard Brinsley Sheridan the perfect riposte. Asked why he was sitting so calmly across the street in the Piazza Coffee House watching the inferno rage he replied: "May not a man be allowed to drink a glass of wine by his own fireside?"

Public safety is a paramount concern, for fire not only destroys buildings. Sadly, on 5th September 1887, 186 people alone were killed in the Theatre Royal, Exeter fire and, by an uncanny coincidence on that same day, 75 people were killed when the Exeter Theatre in New York burnt down.

The last theatre to be badly damaged by fire in London was the Savoy in 1990 though the Iron worked its purpose for, being in, only the auditorium was completely gutted.

So, please remember Mr Jet, and should you hear the name, take heed and action.

* *"Mister Sands" is also commonly used for this purpose.*

Rake Many of our older theatres have rakes. These are sloped floors, varying in the severity of the degree, stretching downwards from the back wall of the stage to the footlights.

They were originally put in to help foster the illusion of perspective but can play havoc with both scenery and ankles. To counter this, new sets incorporate level stage floors which are placed on top of the rakes. Auditoriums are also generally raked. This is to enable persons of restricted growth to have a rare, unimpeded view of life through the fourth wall.

Setting Line (the)

Is that imaginary line which runs across the stage directly above the house curtain and is so called because nothing should be set below it, be that furniture, flats or stiffly posed actors, unless the director wants them to be in full view of the audience when the curtain is in.

For that matter nothing should be straddled over it – not only are the tabs above but also the iron – so leave it clear unless you want to witness a rather blunt version of the guillotine in action.

Speech The gift of speech should not be confused with the art of speaking. Most of us are granted the first, but only those of us lucky enough to enter the worlds of the stage, politics or religion can bore the rest of the world with the latter.

Spot a Dead

Is not only something a lynx-eyed usher observes 15 minutes after curtain down huddled in D13 of the Stalls. It is a term that also applies with the same ophthalmic precision, to master carpenters or production managers when they, from the safety of the stalls, give the definitive height for the dead of any masking material flown.

St Paul's, Covent Garden

Is the Actors' Church. It was designed by Inigo Jones who created masques for Charles I and Henrietta Maria and, as it opened in 1633, predates Wren's Cathedral. It has been associated with the theatre since 1662. It was on 9th May of that year that Samuel Pepys wrote in his diary that he had seen an Italian puppet show performed under the church's portico. This is the first English mention of a Punch and Judy show. Since then, an immense selection of actors, famous and obscure, have been associated with St Paul's, though none have outlived Mr Punch. Their commemorative plaques cover the church walls and though the graveyard can no longer accommodate thespian bones, the flowerbeds have been known to occasionally receive actors' ashes. This practice is not encouraged or for that matter allowed, so if your late old mate insists on being sprinkled there, first study a DVD of The Wooden Horse or The Great Escape and then have copies made of the sand-dispersal socks to place inside your trousers.

Tab Warmers

Is the name for an FOH lighting state plotted into the LX board so as to give vibrant life and extra colour to those old tabs above.

Tidge it in/out

A technical command used when asking for a flying piece to be lowered in or raised out inch by inch with the most delicate precision. The visual result can be almost imperceptible – until it crashes into the deck or grid.

Tumbler (a)

Was a type of vaudeville/variety acrobat whose speciality was, conveniently, tumbling. With somersaults no longer being the draw they used to be, this act is not often encountered professionally these days. However, I am glad to say that the practice still carries on at an amateur level at theatre parties, even if the outcome is invariably A&E.

Twirlies

You may have guessed already but twirlies are indeed the ladies and gentlemen of a musical's ensemble. They are fundamentally different from their near relatives, the turns, for that species, being actors in a musical, speak clearly and move their legs to the left and right though seldom at the same time.

Twirlies, by comparison, are capable of completing full circles of the stage whilst executing graceful arm and leg movements at the same time. They sing loudly to the top of, and above, their vocal range.

Unmentionable (the)

Is, dare I mention it, *Macbeth*. Though the shortest of the Bard's tragedies, has had an ill reputation for longer than any other play in theatrical history. Trouble started on its first performance, which some claim to have been on 7th August 1606, at Hampton Court in the presence of King James I. We are told that Hal Berridge, the boy actor playing Lady Macbeth, did become feverish and died. His death was the start of a catalogue of disasters and accidents that have marred productions ever since. The list of leading actors hurt is impressive and includes Mrs Siddons, Sybil Thorndike, Orson Welles, and Charles Heston, whose tights caught on fire.

The set collapsed at a dress rehearsal at the Royal Court in 1928 seriously injuring many, Olivier just missed being flattened by a falling counterweight in 1937, and a production in 1942 witnessed the deaths of two Witches and a Duncan and the suicide of the set designer.

Some accidents are self-inflicted. Diane Wynyard chose to play the sleepwalking scene with her eyes closed and fell predictably fifteen feet into the pit.

Others are inflicted. Many an actor has been run through in the battle scenes and one, Harold Norman, was killed by a sword thrust at the Oldham Coliseum in 1947.

One logical reason given for all these misfortunes is that, as the play is mostly set at night, poor lighting is to blame. However, actors, being superstitious, have learnt that it's best to respect the dim unknown. They refer to it as 'The Scottish Play', for the title itself, if spoken brings ill luck. Should it be said, the culprit must leave the dressing room, turn around three times, spit, swear, knock thrice on the door and beg to be admitted.

I myself have seen … I'm sorry. I must conclude this section. My pencil has just stabbed me violently and snapped in half.

Weather (the)

Is one important, if overlooked, factor that can determine a show's fortunes.

If it's snowing you'll lose audiences

If it's foggy you'll lose audiences

If it's raining you'll lose audiences

If it's sunny you'll lose audiences

And if it's a heat wave you'll lose your cast.

Xylophone (a)

Should never be carried into a pit upside down.

Nick Bromley

Dance Floors

Introduction

DanceUK advises that: *"The ambition to place dance at the heart of our communities, available for everyone to participate in, must be tied-in with ensuring that every community has access to suitable dance spaces with safe appropriate flooring. To do this, local councillors and town planners need to be made aware of the importance of special flooring for dance activities. Also, the manifesto goal for government to continue to support the creation and maintenance of new specialist dance studios and theatres must ensure these new spaces are built with the correct flooring. It is imperative that all new buildings are properly planned and architects are briefed."*

Why dance requires a special type of floor

For dancers, whether professional, amateur, student or young beginner the dance floor is a place of work where safety and fitness for purpose are essential legal requirements. As with elite sports people and the millions of others participating in some form of sport or physical activity, access to the appropriate equipment for dancers is vital. Because the floor is such a critical element for dancers, floors specifically for the purpose of dance have been developed. General-purpose floors for industrial, commercial and even for sports, simply do not have the right characteristics.

Benefits unique to dance floors

The main criterion for dancers of the dance performance surface is slip resistance, disconcertingly dubbed 'traction' by many in the dance community, With increasing awareness of health and safety legislation, it is also advisable to consider the possibility of a sprung floor, even if building construction and budget eventually preclude it. Lower limb problems such as tendonitis 'shin splints', knee pain and ankle strain can all be attributed to incorrectly specified sprung floors and can take several weeks of physiotherapy and recovery time to correct.

Two terms relevant to dance floors and related to the degree of spring are:

Point Elasticity which describes the degree of deflection or 'give' at the point of contact, landing from a jump for example and

Area Elasticity which describes the spread of the deflection and should be such as to prevent interference with other dancers.

Why other floors are unsuitable for dance

It is a common assumption that a well-designed sports floor will suit the needs of dancers, but there are two intrinsic differences: the performance surface and the construction of the sprung subfloor. Although sports people share the abhorrence of the risk of slipping and falling, they are generally protected by their footwear from floors that might be considered a slip hazard for dancers, for example some hard lacquered wood floors. Along with some shock absorption, most indoor sports require a high degree of energy return and a requirement for adequate ball bounce, Evidently, dancers have scant interest in ball bounce, but they are vitally focused in a different way on a combination of shock absorption and energy return. With respect to spring there are no hard and fast rules, but it is clear that female dancers tend towards shock absorption without any 'sponginess' – whereas men appreciate a dance floor with more 'spring' for their often more energetic choreography. Indoor sports people can tolerate a stiffer floor as they usually wear cushioned footwear – a luxury barred to dancers.

Dance floor surfaces are various constructions of vinyl sheet, differing critically from commercial grade vinyls in that they are formulated to give controlled slip resistance. They are, however, not virtually 'non-slip' like some rubber floors, a property which blocks movement and is a hazard to dancers. It is estimated that over a third of commercial grade vinyl floors are classified as safety floors i.e. slip-resistant, especially in wet conditions, and it would be tempting to think of them as 'safe' for dance. But this slip-resistant property is variously achieved by the addition of coarse abrasive components and/or cork, frequently enhanced by a distinct surface emboss. All of these modifications are the abomination of dancers, who require a smooth and relatively soft surface to avoid abrasion and skin burns.

What components make up a dance floor?

The various components that make up a dance floor system include:

- The performance surface – choice of vinyls selected according to style of dance and footwear
- The sprung subfloor
- The underlying subfloor at the venue
- Impervious membrane to secure against damp
- Doorway ramps
- Disabled access
- Methods for joining rolls – tape, welding options, adhesives

The key elements of a dance floor comprise building floor construction and the dance floor system to be laid on it. The underlying existing floor may be solid or suspended – anything from a quarry-tiled screed to a suspended wood floor with carpet. It is beyond the scope here to offer design solutions to all combinations, but generally they can be found. Sprung floors exist which may be laid directly onto carpet or onto evenly smooth-tamped concrete – a phone call or e-mail to a specialist dance floor manufacturer will help pinpoint the correct solution.

Planning for a new dance floor

In specifying a dance floor there are a number of basic considerations, some of which may require discussion with a dance floor manufacturer and, of course, budget which will generally dictate the final choice.

What dance styles do you perform or teach?

Footwear for different styles of dance may range from barefoot, socks, ballet shoes to tap shoes – even trainers – so it is important to choose a surface that is appropriate to the forms of dance performed. There are, for example, dance surfaces with characteristics appropriate to the following important dance forms.

- Ballet
- Modern/contemporary
- Jazz (stage dance)
- Tap/percussive
- A combination of the above
- Other: e.g. flamenco, ballroom ethnic/folk

Again, it is recommended to ask advice from a specialist dance floor manufacturer.

Portable or permanent flooring?

Another important decision is whether the floor will be loose laid or permanently installed within the fabric of the building. Consider the following possibilities:

- Floors to roll out for a show or class then store away until next time. e.g. in a theatre, school or multi-purpose facility
- Floors for touring and assembly at different venues.
- Floors for permanent installation – check who owns the studio space, do you require approval to install? If you are a tenant, you may be unable within the terms of the lease to install a floor permanently.
- Are you likely to move elsewhere in the foreseeable future and need to take the floor with you?

- How big is the space available?
- What about doors/access and obstructions. Bear in mind that providing access ramps for the disabled may restrict dance floor area.
- Is there sufficient height above the floor for jumps?
- Durability – floors will last a long time. What guarantees are offered?
- Budget – it's a long term investment and important to get it right.

New buildings and refurbishment projects

For larger projects an architect will usually be appointed who will be responsible for specifying the dance floor. The architect will need to consider:

- The importance of user needs vs. aesthetic appeal when specifying.
- Standards and environmental issues.
- Recycling at end of life.
- The role and expertise of the flooring contractor. Most will never have installed a dance floor, so caution is required.
- Normal design criteria apply including:
- Moisture barriers
- Floor strength/construction
- Dance floor thickness/weight
- Ceiling height
- Door swing, are ramps required? See also comment above regarding disabled access.
- Floor or wall mounted dance barres
- Heating system. Under floor heating systems are frequently unsuitable for dance floor construction.

The dance floor performance surface

Whether or not you decide upon a sprung subfloor, you will need to specify the working surface of the dance floor – a most important component. Whilst wood floors are still generally accepted for ballroom, folk and social dance, they have not been the preference of most artistic dancers for over a quarter of a century. Wood in its various forms and finishes (for instance waxed, urethane lacquered or merely sanded) is normally found to be an unpredictable surface for professional dancers. There are people who insist on a wood finish for mixed use and this finish is offered as an option with some sprung floors.

Vinyl dance floors, both (a) compact (i.e. non-cushioned) and (b) with varying qualities of foam backing have been developed both to give slip resistance and point elasticity. Vinyl floors are supplied as rolls and can be rolled up again for storage after use, or permanently installed. When laid down, adjoining areas of vinyl can be taped together for temporary use or 'welded' by various methods for permanent installation. Vinyl floors can be used alone or as a dance surface on a sprung sub floor. A range of vinyl flooring has been developed to meet the various needs of the dance community which includes:

- Vinyl surfaces developed to provide grip or 'traction' demanded by many styles of dance.
- A cushioned vinyl floor additionally offering shock absorption (point elasticity).
- A very thick floor which helps overcome uneven subfloors.

Tougher surfaces to better withstand percussive dance styles such as flamenco and Irish dance. Tap is a particularly aggressive form of dance, and you should be aware that worn and loose screws and taps will damage any dance floor sooner or later so it is important to be vigilant with students' footwear.

Vinyl floors for permanent installation on stages

Before the introduction of vinyl floors during the 1970s, the choice was between a wooden floor and linoleum. Although it may be tempting to opt for a wood surface purely for aesthetic reasons, or a commercial grade vinyl for reasons of cost, today there are many options specifically designed for dance. A well-installed hardwood sprung floor, properly finished and maintained, does look attractive and specifically for ballroom dancing is a desirable option. Softwood floors are rarely an option because even with a lacquered surface they are too readily susceptible to damage, gouging and splintering. With correct preparation and sealing softwood floors can indeed provide a very acceptable subfloor on which to install a vinyl dance surface.

Sprung subfloors

The desire for a floor with 'give' was accelerated by the fashion in ballroom dancing before and after the Second World War. These floors often used coil or leaf springs and, as genuinely sprung floors were too bouncy for ballet or contemporary artistic dance. The need to provide semi-sprung floors, particularly for ballet, has led to considerable modifications in the last 50 years. Metal springs have now largely given way to resilient blocks or pads made of rubbers or polymers. With modern floor construction methods the 'trampoline' effect of those early sprung floors has been suppressed and these modern floors, for both sports and dance, are frequently referred to as semi-sprung. Nevertheless, the distinction has been forgotten and for convenience we loosely refer to both types of floor as sprung floors. Sprung floors, or more accurately semi sprung floors, offer both point and area elasticity. They are most commonly used in permanent installations, in combination with a vinyl (or wood) dance surface. There are also portable panel systems that are suited for touring companies.

Dance floor and studio accessories

In addition to vinyl dance floors and sprung sub floors, when planning a dance studio it is worth considering additional products.

- Care and maintenance products to keep dance floors clean and hygenic.
- Move and store products for storage and transport of vinyl rolls and sprung floor panels.
- A range of tapes, single or double sided, used for joining vinyl strips.
- Ballet barres.

David Brooks

Refurbished stage at Birmingham Hippodrome. Photo courtesy of Birmingham Hippodrome

Recent Developments in Show Intercom Systems

Think of shows, theatre, live events, rock concerts, in fact, the entertainment industry in general. What instantly comes to mind? Yes, it's the lighting, the projections, video screens, the sound system, and the excitement. But where would any live entertainment be without the glue that bonds everything together: communications.

The unsung hero of backstage technology is one which we all take for granted and ultimately rely on for timing, cueing, announcing, and generally keeping the performers and technicians doing the right thing at the right time and at the right place. Of course, we rely on the show intercom system, and unlike its more exciting siblings – light, sound and projection – it has languished in the gloom of analogue for years as digital designs transformed other areas of the entertainment technology business.

"If it ain't broke, don't fix it"

So what's wrong with analogue comms? Sound is analogue after all. We talk analogue, we hear analogue. Simple analogue systems – beltpacks with headsets connected together using mic cable (referred to as simple two-wire partyline systems) – are fine for small shows with a limited number of technicians. As the scale of the show expands, and the number of backstage, sound and lighting technicians increases, the constant chatter on the intercom becomes more of a distraction than information, and the interconnecting cabling can become overwhelming.

A busy show where constant instructions to and from the stage crew, stage manager, sound operator, lighting control and followspots are relayed to all users can quickly descend into chaos, especially if the intercom is the only means of cueing scene changes and lighting or sound effects. So although a two-wire partyline 'daisy-chain' intercom is cheap, simple, easy to use and reliable, its use is limited.

The next step is to expand this simple scheme to have a central main exchange (usually situated conveniently for the stage manager) with individual connections to remote beltpacks. These systems often have up to four channels so that users can be grouped into sound, lighting, and stage crew for example, to reduce the background chatter for those who are not in the group.

What, no wires?

While looking at simple intercoms, some venues and events – even large ones – prefer to rely on walkie-talkie type radio handsets. These tend to be used as point-to-point intercoms, which are used for coordinating events or reporting back, rather than for cueing-type communications.

Enter the matrix

Taking the lead from the telephone industry, the well-tested and traditional method of expanding an intercom system to a wider number of users in different groups has been to incorporate a 'matrix'. This central 'exchange' operates in a similar way to a regular telephone system where the subscriber, or user, makes the connection to another. These systems have additional features not often required with domestic telephones, but which may be included in larger office telephone systems.

The matrix expands the communications system by providing point-to-point communication for individual conversations, but also one to many, or complete conference call options with interrupt functions. Conversations can be parked while more urgent issues are discussed.

Unlike two-wire partyline systems where connections are made from one to the next beltpack in sequence (a 'daisy-chain' wiring scheme), a matrix is located in a central position with wired connections to each outstation. The cost of the matrix unit, which is often defined by the number of 'subscribers', added to the cost of specific cable installation to each outstation location can be significant.

Thank goodness for the digital revolution

When intercom systems embraced digital technology, it not only affected the perceived quality of sound communication, digital also provided product designers with a platform to add more functionality that was no longer hardware, and consequently, cost related. Adding more users, more switching facilities and functions to an analogue system implies more routing circuits, larger matrix cabinets with more pubs and interconnections.

Digital changed that assumption. With software and microprocessors doing the extra work, the relative cost of increasing the capacity of an intercom system (the 'marginal cost' as it's sometimes called) reduced to the cost of extra beltpacks. However, as the scalable nature of an analogue matrix had changed, the actual cost difference between a small and large digital system was quite small, implying, of course, that a small digital intercom system was burdened with a hugely powerful and expensive matrix.

Can small and digital be beautiful?

The immediate answer is, "of course". A specific low capacity, simple digital intercom system is surely possible to design and make at an acceptable market price. But what about the situation where the requirement increases, or a rental or events company wants a standard inventory that can accommodate everything from small TV studio comms to temporary wide area stadium events? Each location, or project would still need a central matrix, and a baseline cost for a matrix that could make the smaller projects unaffordable.

Recent developments in intercom systems have married two sublimely obvious factors of modern technologic life. Firstly, intercoms are needed and used most places in a venue: technical areas, backstage, auditorium, and dressing rooms just about anywhere. And these days, what else is found just about anywhere in a venue? Ethernet. Sockets everywhere. They are now almost as common as power outlets. If they are not available, the cost of running standard Ethernet cable is not high.

Secondly, processing power is plentiful, and memory is cheap. Looking closer at the combination of Ethernet capacity, Ethernet network accessibility, powerful and cheap distributed processing and plentiful memory, and the foundations of a new show intercom philosophy have been laid.

Climbing on the back of Ethernet

It's easy to imagine the questions that appear in the mind: "Do you need a special network for comms only?"... "But if I just connect to that wall outlet, how do I know what that Ethernet network is also connected to?"... "Doesn't the intercom system slow down or disrupt the rest of the Ethernet network?"

An Ethernet-based intercom system can easily reside without affecting any other traffic on the network. In technical terms, it uses a layer 2 multicast system – meaning that messages are sent as a single broadcast to all connected devices, and that is very efficient in terms of bandwidth and is also 'low latency' unlike mobile phones. So there is no need for a dedicated Ethernet network, any available network to which all the users has access will work. It can work with office networks, TV studio computer networks, theatre lighting networks and even the wide area Ethernet networks used with moving lights and LED projection walls on the largest and heavily loaded stadium rock concerts. Outstations can be self-powered, or can pick up power if the network supplies PoE (Power over Ethernet).

The weak link in many intercom solutions is the matrix, as it is a fixed and significant cost whether the system is for two users, three or many hundreds. However, by harnessing current portable processing power and cheap memory, the facilities offered by a matrix can easily be duplicated in each and every outstation. The routing, user-to-user, user to group settings that are held and managed by a conventional matrix can be equally replicated in each intercom beltpack, outstation wall panel, and desk. If the system settings are changed via software on a PC or Mac connected to the same network, the information can be updated immediately to every remote point of the system – even individual beltpacks. And what limits the number of users? Answer: very little. Typically, distributed intercom systems can accommodate between two (yes, just two beltpacks using PoE) to several thousand users, talking to each other or hundreds of groups (rings). How's that for scalability?

Good relations

With so much discussion about the benefits of digital communication over analogue, does this mean the community of analogue users are excluded from the fun of digital?
The answer to that question is simple. Most digital intercom systems are designed to interface with both two and four-wire partyline systems. Interface units

GreenGo from ELC Lighting.

connect between the analogue system cabling scheme and the Ethernet network, and relations can be renewed between the old and the new, with a previously installed analogue network being expanded with digital components.

Features and functionality

Going back to the times of analogue beltpacks and 'everybody talk together' partyline systems, the other useful feature they often had was a call light, and occasionally a 'call/reply' button for rudimentary visual cueing. The latest Ethernet-based digital intercom systems expand the facilities into visual cueing, show relay and even text messaging. This is achieved through the use of LCD displays and push buttons that combine text displays with RGB LED backlights. A bright red display showing the upcoming cue detail that changes to green for go gives an instant and reliable cue.

The range of capabilities with these new systems is available to any outstation, but there are situations where all options will never be used in all locations. For example, a show relay may be needed in a backstage assembly area but communication and cueing is not wanted. A simple wall mounted panel could be the answer. A stage manager would need more functions, and these can be duplicated in several locations for the stage management team to use wherever convenient.

Intuitive programming is the key

There are many digital intercoms systems on the market, and an often-overlooked feature is the programming software. There is no benefit installing a simple intercom system that needs a PhD in computing to program. The latest systems offer downloadable software for both PC and Macs that provide an overview of the 'found' intercom network of outstations, and allow a simple and intuitive method of naming outstations, deciding on groups available for instant access, and who has priority over general group communications. With a PC or Mac in the network acting as a global programming tool, saving all the settings is a click away, and updating the complete system details to all outstation replicas of the 'matrix-style' routing and preferences is achieved almost instantly. So everyone can 'sing from the same song sheet', with perfect cue timing.

Andy Collier

Pepper's Ghost

This was an invention of John Pepper shown at the Royal Polytechnic in London. A ghost illusion was produced by reflecting the static or moving image of an actor concealed from audience view in an area below the stage. The actor was brightly lit, at that time by a limelight lantern, and a large angled sheet of glass was placed at the front of the stage; so the audience saw a composite view of the actor on stage reflected on the inclined glass.

The idea is still in use today, and can be found in the National Sports Museum in Melbourne Australia, Blenheim Palace, the Dickens World attraction at Chatham and in Dover Castle.

From the Ghost's Perspective – FOCUS April/May 2003

Accustomed to my usual attire of the tee shirt, jeans and Doc Martens of a typical lighting techie, it was with some trepidation that I changed into a red evening dress and sheer stockings. It wasn't that posh though, the clothes were well broken-down by the wardrobe department to represent soot stains and I wore a dirty wig and latex mask representing the face of a charred corpse. For I was Sheila, half of the Gruesome Twosome and no-one in the packed house would know it was me.

It was a monologue. Nearing the end of the story the narrator had explained how a close friendship with 'the perfect married couple' turned sour and embittered, and of how her constant harassment of the couple ultimately led to their death by fire. A fire started by the narrator herself whilst armed with petrol and matches. A rather gruesome story, but quite enthralling too.

And so our cue grew near. We took our positions in the darkened cubicle behind the slanting glass. It was rather claustrophobic – pitch black and nothing to see. We could, however, hear the narrator's last few words spoken as she filled a glass from a wine bottle:

"Yes, this was an odd sort of present. It came in the post. I think it was actually sent by Martin. It had no card or anything but I recognised the writing. It arrived a couple of days before they died. In fact he must have posted it the day after we made love. I presume he meant it as some sort of thank you. Well long overdue if I may say so! He certainly never said thank you to me at the time, that's for sure. Anyway, this is no time for grudges. Here's to them both. Martin and Sheila. And the Fearsome Threesome."

And as she drank and keeled over from her poisoned wine a spotlight faded up on us and we raised our glasses of revenge to our tormentor.

A gasp of surprise was raised by the audience who had just witnessed their first viewing of Pepper's Ghost.

But behind the scenes there was nothing to be afraid of – they couldn't see me beneath my ugly mask; and I couldn't see them – just the reflection of my own charred self in the glass, along with Martin, my fellow corpse, who by day was an ASM.

My thanks to Sir Alan Ayckbourn for his permission to quote (and slightly paraphrase) from his late-night thriller 'The Fearsome Threesome'.

Jackie Staines

There's an App for That!

Blissfully, we are through the days where the most common refrain is "there's an app for that". These days we utilise the technology without thinking about it, as an extension of our ability and as a saleable commodity. Yes, there are apps for everything you can think of – changing your baby, counting calories and even an app the sets music to words. For a technologically hungry theatre professional there are a myriad of choices to make our jobs easier and mean that we can share, operate and note on our phones and tablets whilst distributing lists to the whole team.

For the hard core LX folk there are lighting control apps, Most notably the Luminair 2.3 iPhone app which now is available for iPad as well. This controls DMX wirelessly – no more shouting to a board op. It works with colour mixing LED fixtures, studio lighting, moving lights, and any other DMX enabled equipment. It can be used as a focus remote, and even has a feature called 'stacks' which enables live playback. You can now operate a show from your phone. Colour wheels and Gobo catalogues are available; however the ultimate in colour selection is the Selador app from ETC.

There is also AutoCAD ws, a handy viewer so that your designs are always in your pocket, and whilst everybody knows all about their craft you can't beat the Lighting Handbook app, a go to guide for over 900 fixtures, dimmers and boards with illustrations and diagrams.

For our friends in sound we have Audio Tools – running around the auditorium shouting balance tweaks to a technician in a control box are a thing of the past. Decibel meters for louder gigs and the ability to edit sound clips on the way to the theatre. As with lighting there are controls that offer playback – you can have CSC show control software running in your pocket.

Stage management hasn't been left out at all… In fact, we are the best furnished of all in the world of apps. Show tools SM was the first to hit the market; it records spikes with colour codes, has a setting checklist and a props list, organisable by scene. The most impressive feature is the show timer, excellent for those of us that struggle with calculating time. We have note taking and sharing with Evernote, The Complete Works of Shakespeare (searchable with Glossary) in our backpacks and even Scene Mate, an app to help actors learn their lines.

The newest blocking software – Stage Write, made quite an impact when it was launched earlier this year. Although the price, coming in at £139.99, is somewhat prohibitive for the majority of freelance stage managers, I can see how it is a very useful tool. Once you have drawn your set you can create actor icons that reside in the green room, and then move them about the set. The most useful function is the 'traffic flow' allowing you to record groups moving around. There is a trial version that has most of the features, and if you haven't already it's well worth downloading to have a look.

Formations Elite is a more affordable alternative, coming in at £6.99. Designed to record staging it's not quite blocking as such, but can record formations on grids and even has icons for people and instruments, even flags and trees. This again is printable and sharable.

The big thing missing from all incarnations of these apps is the ability to link the images and movements to points in a script, which means that there is no time saved when you have to collate all the information afterwards. It's all very interesting, and useful to record after a show goes up to share and archive, however for the rehearsal process I am yet to find anything more efficient that my mind and a pencil.

As a stage manager the apps that I find most useful are the find friends app to locate lost performers and the London Transport app to get everybody home. Hailo – the app that lets you summon a black cab, and pay for it by credit card has been a revelation on late Sunday nights. Fast, easy and no more waiting on street corners or struggling to find cash machines.

There are two other apps that are worth a mention, both with superb concept and beauty – There's Richard Pilbrow's Theatre Project, A backstage adventure tracking the development of creative professions backstage. The second belongs to The Royal Opera House, who has recently launched an app called 'The Show Must Go On' in association with Hide and Seek as a result of the recent Nesta initiative pairing arts foundations with digital companies. This is an app aimed at younger users that launches the player into a world of production, where each element of a show has to be managed and completed before the curtain goes up. Excellent fun for the hardened professional, as well as a gentle induction to those kids heading into the industry.

At the moment innovation is affecting theatre at a staggering rate, and with the development of apps we are seeing more and more ways integrating our phones into our working lives. There very nearly is 'an app for everything'.

Sharon D Calcutt

This article appears by kind permission of The Stage *and* Sightline.

EDUCATION

Footsteps on the Ladder ...

I went to a grammar school in south London. It had a large hall with a good size raised stage: wings, borders and a fancy set of royal blue tabs.

The lighting had never been upgraded and was pretty much as installed in the fifties: battens, a handful of Patt 60s, 23s and 123s. Eleven ways of Furse resistance dimmers provided control, a twelfth had caught fire and been removed. For some reason I thought that it all looked rather interesting, and was certainly preferable to having to appear on the stage in person. There was an active drama group which involved pupils, 'old boys', and parents and produced fairly elaborate productions in the summer, such as *Oh What A Lovely War* in Falmouth, and Man Of La Mancha in Exmouth.

The Latin master (in charge of technical issues to do with the stage) was looking for someone to take over as the two sixth formers who previously "did" the lights were leaving that year. After expressing an interest I was handed the keys to the lighting box (prompt side wings, no view) and left to my own devices. Under the stage I found two Patt 223s, some ancient rolls of Cinemoid, and spent several happy hours playing around, re-arranging the rig and colouring lamps. The lighting box soon had a crew, kettle and an ashtray, and we experienced quite a few electric shocks and memorable and alarming ladder moments.

This activity was noticed and it turned out that a grant for additional equipment was available. At the end of the summer holiday boxes of shiny green 123s and 23s turned up, along with a 24 way 2-preset control board and dimmer pack. We bought more Cinemoid, and a knife, a set of spanners, and a big jar of instant coffee.

The following year, our English teacher (who directed the plays) organised a school trip to see Hair at the Shaftesbury Theatre. We were sitting in the upper circle directly in front of a window behind which a tiny room housed an organ-like console, an operator, and a dog. A few of us went to the Oporto pub after the show and found the operator in there, quite happy to chat to an over excited 17-year-old. The electrics department was very kind and arranged a trip to see the rig and the control system. A few weeks later I had a relief showman's job, presetting the CD150. I spent my upper sixth between the school stage and traveling up to the West End in the evenings. I did some A levels too, largely thanks to the art teacher who used to let me doze for a bit in the studio after assembly.

That school stage with its assorted lanterns, mis-matched nuts and bolts and broken Grelcos was a wonderland that shaped the rest of my life. I have been lucky enough to have made a living in lighting ever since. The move from technician to designer was facilitated through rock & roll touring and then industrial theatre. A lucky break, working as an unpaid assistant to David Hersey, eventually lead to the collaboration that formed DHA Design in 1983.

Whether a small theatre with a few spots, a theme park full of expensive kit, an expo or a museum, the craft is the same and in order to learn it, you need to get up a ladder, put your hands on a light and see what it can do. Look, practice, stand back and look closely again. Learn about the equipment and the control systems, the drafting and rendering. At some point you might want to go into architectural lighting, in which case drawing packages such as Autocad and Vectorworks are widely used, as well as technical programs such as Dialux for checking light levels, and rendering through packages such as 3D StudioMax and Photoshop.

But even though so much of the art is reliant on the craft – the controls and connections, the miles of wires and realms of paperwork – don't get bogged down in the nuts and the bolts. Above all try and learn the art. And then you will know, because it will just 'look right'.

Light is fluid, try and get out of the way and let it come through. And collaborate. Listen carefully to the other people in the team. Work for nothing if you can't get paid, at least until you can get to a point where you might be paid a little. And always try and get something in the board no matter what is going on around you. Having a rough focus, a set of cues or 'looks' to come back to and then refine gives you the beginnings of a structure. Even if you throw half of it away later, it gets the process moving. And then there you are, close to that wonderful point (in any lighting process) when you just know that the heart of the design is right, and you can then sit back and enjoy gently smoothing out all the rough edges, with the technology working with you, not against you.

Adam Grater

True Theatre in Education and the Curtain Theatre

Back in 1964 when I was appointed to run one of the first Educational Theatre Centres in the country for the London County Council, most of the work was with Amateur Drama Groups who were enrolled at one or other of the Adult Education Institutes but had little or no staging facilities for performance.

The 1930's vintage Toynbee Theatre had been closed for some years due to a dispute between the Authority and Toynbee Hall, but once open again, the groups soon came flooding back – but under a new charter. Previously, it had been customary for a group to book two, three, four maybe five performances at a venue, with an extra day for dress rehearsal. That was as much as any group could afford in rent. They would bring their own scenery (if any), props, costumes, etc and, making the best of the very limited time available, all would be erected and set up in a bit of a jumble in time for a rather ragged rehearsal – usually lit while the rehearsal proceeded – and somehow or other the curtain went up on time (nearly) for the first night.

My job was to try and improve on this scenario and make the well-meaning enthusiasts aware of the stagecraft which would improve the presentation of their play and give far greater satisfaction to the back-stage team in the process. As the theatre and the group were both working under the umbrella of the education authority, there was no charge, so no need for economy on preparation time, so I would ask the director concerned to bring that backstage team along for a production meeting at least six weeks before the production went on stage. ("What backstage team?" I might hear).

Well at least, this was a timely warning that a team must be found. At the production meeting, I would advise about the setting for the play and time would be booked in the theatre workshop over the weeks prior to the production for the team to draw the necessary flats, etc from the theatre stock, to mix and apply paint and create a professional-looking effect on stage. If it were a realistic setting then the aim was to produce something that looked like a real bit of architecture rather than a row of canvas flats. Those responsible for lighting the show would be trained in the operation of the old Grand Master board and shown how to achieve the effects the director asked for; similarly any sound requirements would be discussed and training given where necessary.

Even if they were only to give two or three performances, the group would move into the theatre the previous week-end to build their set, light it and make any necessary sound recordings so that all would be ready for a technical rehearsal on the Monday evening, dress rehearsals on the Tuesday and Wednesday and the performances on the Thursday and Friday. This was a tough learning curve for some, of course, but the results were generally encouraging and, in some cases, impressive.

From my own point of view, this meant that I was working very hard over each and every week-end and weekday evening, but, apart from some managerial duties, on weekdays I was reasonably free. Nevertheless, it was tiring, but the back-up from the Authority was strong and I was soon given a few hours of secretarial assistance and cover for a few evenings from a fellow professional.

One morning I had a telephone call from a drama teacher in a south London school: "I hear the old Toynbee Theatre is open again. Would it be possible for me to bring my fourth years over to have a look backstage?" Having little to do that week during the day, I fixed up for an afternoon visit and asked the school-keeper to stand by to give me a little assistance. There was a set on-stage of course for the performance that night, but I had closed the house curtain. There were over 20 boys and girls in the party, very animated by this out-of-school excursion, but as I led them into the auditorium and the plush seats and awesome atmosphere had an immediate calming effect.

I explained a little about the theatre and what we did there before calling to the school-keeper to open the house tabs and invited them to come up the steps onto the stage. They didn't need asking twice. We talked about the set for a while and how it was constructed before starting our tour. It was quite a large party to get into some of the off-stage positions but with a good bit of shoving and moving around, they all managed to see what was going on. We saw the winch that opened and closed the curtain and some of them tried it. We saw the wind machine and they *all* had to try it. Same with the thunder sheet. Then they saw the lighting gantry and watched a couple of cues being executed. Next the sound gantry, the prompt corner and cueing system and finally down to the workshop.

Then they all trooped back into the auditorium where they had some questions to ask me before setting off back to school. The teacher involved phoned me the following morning full of thanks and praise and I marked the event as a one-off. But no, the word got around and during the rest of that term I had seven or eight other schools who brought parties for a backstage tour.

They all went away well satisfied but I was unhappy about it. Theatre is a live art and I was showing it to these pupils in a dead form. Nothing was *happening*; where was the drama, the play? So I concocted a little playlet in two short scenes around a few sound effect records that I had: a dog barking, seagulls, a motor boat, etc. There were two characters, but a number of light cues, sound cues, some live (the wind machine of course) some on tape and props to be moved during the scene change. Of course, it had to be done in the existing setting which changed weekly and I couldn't interfere with the lighting layout for that evening and had to write a plot around it. Still, the youngsters could now do an actual play. They would sit and watch a read-through with two of their number reading the parts and being directed where to move, followed by the backstage tour which was now far more related to a script.

The school-keeper had become very enthusiastic about these visits and was taking on far more duties as my assistant, so we could divide the party into two groups for the tour. Then I allocated duties: two of them up to the lighting board; two to the tape recorder, two to the prompt corner, two ASMs either side of the stage and two actors. The rest would sit in front and watch until it was their turn to take over one of the positions. I would be up on the lighting gantry to help the two on the board and from there I could also watch the prompt corner which was just underneath. The school-keeper would watch the off-stage people doing live effects and the scene change and with luck, the teacher would look after the actors.

So we would start a halting run through scene 1. It was pretty chaotic to begin with of course but gradually they got the hang of the cueing system and with many changes of jobs and loud prompts from those in the auditorium, they struggled through the short script. By the time everyone had tried every position, the final performance was relatively smooth. Concentration was intense, arguments had subsided and, most importantly, they were working as a team and acknowledging the need for a leader - the stage manager in the prompt corner.

During the following months, the news got around the local schools about this free afternoon excursion and applications to book a visit mushroomed until I was sometimes getting two, even three visits a week. The difficulty was that there was always a different set on the stage into which I had to adapt our little playlet and the lighting plot had to be rewritten to fit the layout for the current production. At the end of that school year I decided that there was sufficient demand to justify taking the theatre away from the adults for a couple of weeks each term and designing and building a special set for what I was now calling the Stage Management Exercise. I could light it properly and far more effectively, props and furniture would be our own, not the visiting group's and the experience would be far more authentic for the youngsters. And so it proved.

As time passed, the L.C.C. became the G.L.C.; the department for education for Inner London Schools became the I.L.E.A.; and the Toynbee Theatre became the Curtain Theatre. As the work with schools increased, so the theatre staff increased.

There was a marked decline in bookings from adult amateur groups. Some of our regulars had folded through lack of numbers; others had found venues nearer to where they operated. However, projects with schools increased to fill the available space. The Authority spent considerable sums on buying large blocks of seats for matinée performances at the National Theatre or the R.S.C. It became very evident to us that much of those visits were wasted when the pupils had had no preparation so, in association with the theatres concerned, we offered a three-part programme. Part 1 consisted of a workshop on the main themes of the play that were going to see. Part 2: the actual performance at the National or wherever and Part 3, a return to the Curtain for a follow-up session with a member of the cast or the director.

Another very popular project was what we called Simulation Exercises and these involved the visiting school party completely. We would take a subject of some social significance, cast the key roles amongst ourselves and divide the youngsters into relevant departments. One such dealt with a problem with a single-parent family where the mother needed to go into hospital but the man with whom she was cohabiting was opposing hospitalisation and was ill-treating the two young children.

The school party were either trainee social workers, doctors, educational welfare officers, trainee NSPCC officers, journalists, etc. Every one of them at some time during the morning had to visit the flat (a totally believable creation on the stage) and met with hostility and non-cooperation. The children, apparently, were at their grandmas that morning. Returning to their departments (in the theatre dressing rooms) which were all linked by telephone, they discussed how they could best help the situation in the children's best interests and the afternoon was taken up with a case conference where all the agencies came together to make their final decision.

Another subject was Town Planning. We invented a fictitious dock in the East End which was up for redevelopment. We made a model of what it might look like with a collection of photographs to bring the area to life and the youngsters were again in different departments: Tower Hamlets Planning Dept, Health and Social Security, education, environment, plus a couple of local action groups. With a little prompting, they suggested new housing projects, a little light industrial area, a park and an attractive riverside walk. Certain features they wanted to keep including the Admirals House, an 18th Century listed building and a row of cottages all occupied by elderly people, etc. At the tea break, the model was on show in the cafe and as they were crowding round it and feeling very confident in what they wanted to do, a journalist mingled with the group and quite casually asked one of them what they thought about the new container depot which he'd heard was to occupy the whole site (blatant use of theatrical conflict!).

There was uproar of course and they returned to their departments to consider what action to take to defend their plans. The telephones were very busy. In the afternoon there was an official enquiry held in the theatre under the Chairmanship of an independent investigator. The very smooth American representative of the company who wished to build the container depot put his case and then a spokesman from each department had the chance to speak up for their side of the argument.

Many of those youngsters who had never in their lives spoken publicly before gave impassioned speeches to save their pet projects and on one occasion, a young girl was very nearly in tears in her defence of the old people in the row of cottages which might be demolished.

Other work was designed to help teachers introduce an examination text: courses in lighting, sound editing and scene painting for teachers and for pupils. Work in association with the London museums, particularly the Tower of London where we would base a programme on some historical personality that had been imprisoned there and retry the case through modern eyes. A good deal of work was aimed at junior pupils also and most of them had their first experience of live theatre when they visited the annual Christmas play in the latter half of the autumn term, a specially written piece in panto style with a good story and lots of broad fun.

But the Stage Management Exercise remained the project that teachers demanded most. Eventually we had six playlets, all fully staged, one of which would be brought back from stores on a biennial basis. There was a cut version of the first three scenes of *Hamlet* (much use of dry ice and green spots), Conan Doyle's *The Speckled Band* (the snake came down the bell rope *and up again!*); *Scrooge*, a shortened version of *A Christmas Carol*, *The Curse of Castle Reeking* (with use of gauze and vamp trap), and *The Burning of Baker's Barn*, a domestic tragedy complete with more dry ice, flame projection and trick falling masonry. But the original story, which became *The Cliff Top Mystery* was ever popular and even ran into a junior version, as did *Scrooge*. But the overriding principal throughout all the work with pupils was at some point to put them in the driving seat and to encourage them to think on their feet, to communicate and to work together as a team and to practice leadership.

The Curtain celebrated 25 years' service to the Authority in 1989 with a production of Priestly's *An Inspector Calls*. But it was a celebration with a sting in its tail. The lease of the theatre from our landlord, Toynbee Hall, was due to run out. Efforts were made to find another suitable building but fate stepped in in the person of the redoubtable Margaret Thatcher who was in the act of dismantling the top-heavy GLC and in so doing, abolished the Inner London Education Authority and returned education to the Boroughs.

The justification for the Curtain and its permanent staff of 13 by this time, was that it served *all* the schools of Inner London. No one Borough could possibly afford us. So during that summer, all the equipment that we had striven so hard to acquire and to keep up to date, was transferred to a Drama Centre in Camden. There were no positions for the majority of the staff, all specialists in their field, in other education establishments but happily, they all found employment within nine months of the closure. Nevertheless, it was with a heavy heart that I handed in my keys to the Curtain Theatre in September that year.

Donald Walker

A stage manager's challenge.

Expectations of Students Starting a University Lighting Course

If you are thinking about going to university or drama school to study lighting, its useful know what tutors are looking for. There are several dedicated theatre and performance lighting design degree courses, and a number of other courses where aspects of stage lighting practice are a major part of the course. Each one has a different focus, and therefore each values slightly different things in its candidates. Do some research into the courses and what they offer, but also into the kinds of jobs graduates go on to do.

The websites of the Association of Lighting Designers (www.ald.org.uk) and the Association of British Theatre Technicians (www.abtt.org.uk) are a good starting point.

It is often said that lighting – especially theatre and concert lighting – is not so much a job as a way of life. If you decide to do it for a living, you will often be working when everyone else is either playing or asleep, and most people will have no idea what it is you actually do! If you like that idea then go for it, but if you don't, perhaps you need to think again.

Pre-Entry Qualifications

There is no A-level in stage lighting, and Btecs vary a lot in how much lighting they include, so most Higher Education courses in lighting will not ask for anything specific, or rule out any subject. If you are taking multiple qualifications, such as A-Levels or Scottish Highers, my advice is to study subjects you enjoy, and at which you are most likely to get good grades.

It is almost certain that BSc courses will ask for specific pre-entry qualifications in maths and science. Most higher education course in lighting areas value good GCSE maths and science or equivalent too, though BAs are typically less specific about what they want in terms of post 16 qualifications. You should be able to find out if the courses you want to do require any particular qualification from the institution's web site or from UCAS. If in any doubt – get in touch with the institution.

So, you might start your university study of lighting with maths physics and chemistry, with English literature, drama and art, or with a Btec. All of these qualifications, and many others, cover topics and teach skills that are useful to a lighting student. So there will be useful things you have

Students preparing for a technical rehearsal. Among the many laptop computers is the ETC Eos lighting desk and a Northern Light stage management console (far left).

learnt that others have not, and gaps that you will need to fill that others do not – just like every other student on your course.

A Lighting Portfolio

Many courses, especially those focussing on lighting design, ask candidates to bring a portfolio to interview. This can be quite intimidating. First thing to do is to read through everything the course has sent you by way of instruction or advice on what to bring. Next, here are some tips:

- Quality scores much higher than quantity. Make sure it is possible to see everything you have in your portfolio in five minutes – maximum!
- Pick the best examples of everything. Six to 12 pages of high quality at A3 or even A4 is much better than big folders stuffed with tatty scripts and posters.
- Print all your images on good quality paper using a decent printer, or, make an e-portfolio (see below). Don't include anything you're not proud of.
- Test the effectiveness of your portfolio out on someone who will be honest with their feedback (so probably not mum and dad – sorry folks).
- Do your research – and show you have more than a passing interest in lighting.
- Name the LDs that inspire you, include pictures of their work (search the web if you have to).
- If you have realised work, include the lighting plan – but, make it look good.
- Include notes or images about what inspires your own work.
- Your research shows the depth of your interest, and helps to convince a tutor you will stick with the course for the full 2, 3 or 4 years.

e-Portfolio

If you don't have access to good quality printing (or can't afford it, it can be quite expensive) ask if you can bring your portfolio digitally. (If it's on a disc or USB stick, make sure that whatever you bring with you can be read by someone else's computer! Try it out to be sure.) Powerpoint and Prezi both offer relatively simple ways to display pictures, scans of documents, and PDFs of plans, and annotations. Many photographs of stage lighting look at their best on a screen – but remember to include a caption to tell the viewer what they are looking at.

If you include a 'show-reel' or video extracts from work you have done – again, pick highlights and make sure the whole thing won't run too long (or it won't get watched all the way through!)

(Note: make sure there and no confidential or embarrassing files also on the disc or USB stick!).

If you are applying after some time away from school or college

First of all – don't rule yourself out if you don't have great qualifications from school or college. UCAS points scores are usually of less importance than experience, but do make sure you ask if this is the case for the courses you wish to apply for. Try to get a professional reference that shows you know what paid work is all about – in theatre, concerts or events – and that you are able to stick to a task. Your potential tutors will want to know that you are able to turn up every day and be enthusiastic.

In summary:

Do your research – about the course, but also about the jobs you expect the course to prepare you for. Find out what its like to do what you want to do for a living.

Demonstrate that you know what you are getting yourself into – you are applying to study for 'a way of life, rather than just a job' and most lighting courses demand a substantial time commitment.

If at all possible, go to an open day, and talk to current students (and if possible graduates and people working in the industry already).

Try to be clear in your own mind about whether you get your kicks from *how* or *why,* and chose courses that will let you focus on which ever one you chose.

At school or college, study subjects you enjoy and will get good grades for, lighting needs all kinds of knowledges. Its a good idea to have reasonable maths, and if you have set your heart on one particular course, check to see if they demand anything in particular.

If you are not applying directly from school or college, experience is likely to count for more than your post 16 qualifications – but check with the course.

If you are asked for a portfolio – quality counts. Include only your best work, and try to get advice from the course about what they like to see.

Good Luck!

Nick Moran

STAGE LIGHTING

New! – the Candle

Suppose that the candle had just been invented. Compared with modern light sources, it has so many merits!

It might be promoted like this:

- Good colour appearance
- Good colour rendering
- Constant colour from batch to batch and throughout life
- Instant ignition
- Full brightness at ignition, no warm-up period
- 100% lumen maintenance through life
- Instant hot restrike
- Silent operation
- No radio interference
- No power supply needed
- No early life failure
- Visual indication of elapsed burning time and remainder of life
- Doesn't explode at end of life
- Rugged construction and simple low-cost packaging
- Single burning position – cap down
- Worldwide availability, at low cost
- No maintenance
- No CE Approval needed, or WEEE Regs, or RoHS compliance (but take care over Health and Safety)
- No mercury, lead, cadmium or chromium content
- Easy landfill disposal

Colour brings life, texture and vibrancy to the stage, I love it.
Richard Pilbrow; Lighting Designer and Consultant UK and USA

A Stage Lighting Timeline

This overview is written by a Welshman writing from Great Britain. The view from elsewhere will be different.

Probably from prehistoric times, performances were in the open air, but perhaps cave dwellers entertained each other in fire light at other times.

Greek plays have lighting references; they took place from sunrise to sunset and the time of day is given for different sections.

c1550 Performances were lit with candles, with light coloured using coloured liquids in bottles in front of candles and beams shaped by bottle lenses and simple reflectors. There are indications that the lighting varied between bright for comedy or happy scenes and much darker for tragedy.

c1630 Candle footlights and side lights are employed with dimming by lowering metal tubes over the candles.

Seventeenth Century. Chandeliers act as principal source of illumination, the audience lit along with the stage.

1783 The oil lamp is invented in France, at first an open burner and then with a glass chimney. Individual lanterns are now possible.

1791 Coal gas can be manufactured in large volumes. Over the next sixty or so years it becomes possible to manufacture gas on site allowing gas to be used for general and stage illumination.

1803 Lime light invented. A block of lime heated with a hydrogen or acetylene flame with a simple lens or reflector makes a small enough source for a true spot light to be possible. An operator is required to control the gas flame.

Early and mid Nineteenth Century. Gas lighting becomes more general, at first with open flame burners and later with mantles – a gauze surround to the flame impregnated with mineral salts which glowed in the heat. Gas meant that the whole installation could be controlled from one place - lighting layouts commonly being footlights with rows of lights overhead and vertically at the sides.

1809 Electric arc lamp invented, although this took some ninety years to be generally used in theatre.

1816 Chestnut Street Theatre in Philadelphia first to be fully gas lit.

1841 Filament light bulb invented, but not really practical as yet.

1846 Carbon arcs used as followspots, but not as efficient as limelight.

c1870 Irving starts the practice of lighting rehearsals to arrange the effects for each scene. Gas lighting makes it possible to dim the auditorium lights during the performance.

1881 Savoy Theatre in London is the first to be lit with electricity.

1882 Munich Exposition provokes great use of electricity: first really practical filament lamps, first use of liquid dimmers. Centralised mechanical control possible with tracker wire operated dimmers

Late Nineteenth Century.

Commercial production of gelatine colour filters: Thomas Digby in Great Britain, Stanhope Brigham in the USA.

Early Twentieth Century.

Development of wire wound resistance dimmers. Carbon arc takes over from limelight for spot lights and projectors. Gas and candle strips superseded by filament lamps, at first dipped in lamp lacquer for colour, later in housings allowing the use of filters.

Direct operated controls with resistance dimmers mounted on the back of the board and connected to handles mounted on shafts. Handles could be locked to the shafts, so many handles could be operated together. "Grand Master" type of control on which individual shafts and the dimmer handles clipped to them could be arranged to work either in the same direction or in reverse making it possible to crossfade.

Smaller installations utilised slider dimmers consisting of resistance wire would round a former, at first of slate, later synthetic. Brush moved directly over the windings by a simple handle. Sliders were common in small installations up until the early 1960s.

Spotlights of simple form with a lens and reflector became common but, with a few exceptions, until the end of the Second World War lighting usually a general flood in a number of colours supplemented by spots, either fixed or following, to highlight individual areas.

c1930s Development of profile spots: in America with a tubular lamps almost enclosed in a semi ellipsoidal reflector (hence generic name of ellipsoidal spots) and in Britain with a round bulb lamp with a mirror behind it and the name mirror spots. These units allowed the beam to be shaped by an iris, by shutters or by metal plates in the gate. Templates (US), Gobos (GB).

Followspots, usually carbon arc source, became available with mirror spot optics as an improvement on the commonly used lens spots.

Reflector spots became available, initially developed in Germany as narrow beam (often low voltage) lanterns; in Britain they became available as medium beam "Acting Area Lanterns" hanging overhead and narrow beam "Pageant" lanterns as side or back light. This type of fixed beam lantern was less common in America until the introduction of the sealed beam – PAR – lamp.

1935 Light Console introduced by the Strand Electric and Engineering Company. Control using a modified Compton organ console to control motorised resistance and transformer dimmers – the dimmer bank effectively a motorised bracket handle board with a clutch arrangement making it possible for dimmers on the same shaft to operate in either direction while the shaft rotated in a constant direction. Console designed (by F.P. Bentham) to allow one person to control a large installation while being able to see the stage.

Late 1930s Acetate colour filter introduced. Principal names in Britain Cinemoid, in the USA Roscolene

1940s Second World War hindered development on both sides of the Atlantic. In the 1940s the Strand Electric Company introduced the Pattern 76 acting area lantern with a spun aluminium body, a first step away from totally hand made sheet metal construction.

1950s First significant development on the lantern front was the introduction of the Pattern 23 Baby Mirror Spot by Strand Electric in 1953. It was the first lantern to be designed for mass production was made from alloy castings and with a very efficient optical system giving pretty well as much light from the newly introduced Class T1 500w lamp as previous 1000w models. Beam shaping on the standard lantern was by iris diaphragm or masks. Use of pre-focus lamp cap eliminated the need for comprehensive controls to centre the lamp in the reflector, a simple slide for peak/flat beam adjustment sufficing.

Sister lantern of similar construction introduced shortly afterwards with the Pattern 123 500w Fresnel spot. These lanterns revolutionised lighting in both small and large theatres. The design principles, although not the cast structure, were copied by other British manufacturers.

The Introduction of the lantern hook clamp was another breakthrough in this decade: a very simple device allowing the lantern to be hung on the bar with the weight taken by the clamp while the clamp was tightened to the bar with a wing bolt. Previous clamps were characterised by the need to tighten the clamp onto the bar with two bolts and then hang the lantern. The hook clamp was, in fact, a simplification of the C Clamp common in America for years.

Developments in electronics in the fifties and sixties led to improvements in control. In Britain these were a system involving thyratron valves to chop the lamp waveform in a similar way to the modern SCR/Thyristor dimmer and developments of the light console to allow accurate setting of dimmer levels using the same motor operated dimmer bank; and the saturable reactor, a system by means of which the impedance of a coil in the lamp feed could be varied using a dc current which allowed the lamp level to be varied from a small fader.

Ability of all these systems to be controlled from banks of small faders meant that comparatively small desks could control large numbers of channels. More or less sophisticated ways were designed to group and master controls and leading to the ability to preset levels for a number of changes in advance of the lighting on the stage.

In Britain it became common to equip theatres with controls having, for the time, large numbers of dimmers. In America, especially on Broadway, the fashion remained of using smaller numbers of large capacity temporary dimmers to control groups of lanterns. These differences led directly to the different practices in the design of memory boards; in Britain boards recorded complete states while in America the "tracking" board recorded only the changes from one state to the next.

1960s Changes in lantern design centred round the smaller lamps becoming available and the general adoption of Tungsten Halogen. Smaller lamps led, obviously, to smaller lanterns and less obviously, to more efficient optical systems. All manufacturers produced ranges of tungsten halogen lanterns. In some cases these were simply modifications of existing designs but later lanterns were introduced designed to take the full benefits of the newer lamps. The move away from sheet metal construction continued.

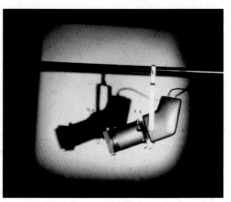

The introduction in 1964 of the Strand Pattern 264 had a great impact at the time but interest waned. An ellipsoidal profile spot using small cap-up lamp, it was distinguished from other profile spots by virtue of having two sets of shutters in the gate, one with conventional straight edges and the other with saw tooth edges. With the straight edge shutters sharp focused the saw tooth set were slightly out of focus. It was therefore possible for the beam to be partially sharp edged and partially soft edged.

The Pattern 23 was redesigned in about 1969 so that all models had shutters and no means of lamp adjustment was necessary.

PAR lamps started to be used in the late 1960s. Starting in America they soon became popular as a way of getting a lot of (coloured) light on stage with minimal cost for the concert industry. They started to be used in conventional theatre productions as a source of very intense light but with no focusability other than rotation of the oval beam. First used in Britain as series pairs with 120v American lamps. 240v lamps soon became available avoiding this necessity.

Control development centred mainly on the development of thyristor dimmers and multi-preset controls with varying facilities for grouping channels together. Memory boards were confined to systems using mechanical memory such as the punched card systems made by Grossmann in Denmark and marketed by Strand as Memocard in Britain. The middle of the decade saw a breakthrough with the release by Strand of the IDM system and by Thorn lighting of the Q File. The latter was developed for BBC television and became popular in TV studios although less so in theatre.

1970s Lantern development in this decade was principally a result of the almost universal use of tungsten halogen lamps with a consequent increase in efficiency and reduction in size of units. The most significant development was the variable beam – zoom – profile spot, at first the CCT Silhouette range and then from other

manufacturers. Acceptance of these lanterns was enthusiastic in Britain but muted in America.

Concert lighting continued to use larger and larger rigs of sealed beam lanterns, both as single units and as units having several lamps in one housing.

Control development in theatre at this time followed on from the 1960s with increasingly successful memory boards from established manufacturers such as Strand, from American companies such as Kliegl and Colortran and from newly established companies. The most important system on this side of the Atlantic was Strand's MMS with the same firm's Light Palette a success in America although a number of Light Palettes were sold here.

1980s and 1990s Lanterns become yet smaller and brighter due to the further development of tungsten halogen lamps. In Britain both Strand and CCT (the latter in conjunction with ADB of Belgium) developed the use of alloy extrusions for lantern manufacture leading to "families" of lanterns using the same extrusions e.g. CCT's Minuette range and Strand's Preludes.

From the end of the seventies moving lights became increasingly common, at first in the concert world and then in theatre. Theatre lanterns which could be reset by remote control had been available for many years, but units were now produced with many in-built effects facilities as well as conventional pan, tilt and focus. Use of discharge lamps gave increased intensity though requiring mechanical dimming and often, for theatre work, colour temperature correction.

Controls increased in complexity with the need to handle many moving lights in a rig. Concerts were frequently operated by the designer and many controls in this world offered great flexibility for devising effects, often at the expense of the repeatability essential for conventional theatre work.

1986 The introduction of DMX512 as a universal, non proprietary control protocol was to enable any desk to talk to any dimmer. The protocol was generally adopted, revised in 1990, in 2004 and again in 2008. Originally intended solely for desk/dimmer communication the protocol was soon adopted to control moving lights and effects equipment.

2000s Desks increasingly designed round control of the many parameters of moving and colour changing lights with less stress on the importance of repeating theatrical cues night after night. Desks characterised  by their ability to handle the large numbers of channels required for such lanterns with sophisticated means of grouping channels and recording channel values for specific orientations of the lantern or setting up "automatic" movement patterns. At first more needed in the concert industry but become increasingly commonly used in theatre.

Discharge light sources, especially in moving lights became common in this period. The obvious disadvantage of the discharge lamp in having a non continuous spectrum which did not match that of the commonly used tungsten equipment being secondary to the vastly greater light intensity available. Dimming of discharge lamps has to be by mechanical means and many lanterns have this facility, often combined with the ability to strobe the light by rapid movement of the dimming shutters.

Automated lights generally fitted with colour changing systems, the simplest being a wheel or scroller, more sophisticated units use systems of filters to vary the amount of, usually, the secondary colours, cyan, magenta and yellow present in the beam and therefore its colour. Lighting desks developed with sophisticated "colour picker" systems to allow the colour to be remotely controlled along with the rest of the lantern.

LED light sources increasingly being used to reduce power consumption and to facilitate colour changing. Early lanterns suffered from poor dimming curves, from colour fringing due to the use of multiple LED sources and from poor colour mixing due to the use of only three LED colours. Development has greatly improved all three aspects. LED lanterns now perform optically as well as tungsten as wash lights with the bonus of greater efficiency when generating saturated colours. Dimming curves are much improved and, at the time of writing, credible LED profile lanterns are appearing.

The rise in the number of channels for each lantern increased the pressure on desk manufacturers to build controls with channel counts that would have been unimaginable when the DMX512 standard was designed. Increasingly controls designed to communicate via an Ethernet protocol, often simply by carrying DMX universes (512 channels) over Ethernet but increasingly by direct Ethernet communication between desk and lantern or dimmer.

Control developments have led to Remote Device Management and Advanced Control Network. The former is an extension of the DMX protocol which allows equipment to be set up remotely from the control. The latter is a future replacement control protocol without the 512 channel limitation and which will allow both remote setting up and also the equipment to "talk back" to the control – for example lamp failure could be notified to the desk.

Wireless DMX systems allow the transmission of DMX data over long distances. Useful for temporary set ups but individual lanterns are now being fitted with wireless facilities which means that it is no longer necessary to have wired DMX available.

Lighting systems are becoming increasingly complex electronically to offer more and more facilities to the user and this trend shows no sign of abating.

Philip L. Edwards

Shabatoi, a rock musical in New York shimmered in a world of mysticism and divinity. Broad walls of deeply coloured light in glossy blues to intense lavenders. Gel strings included blues and blue-greens which painted the actors and costumes with deep rich bases against which the crisp practicals and keylights set off their faces and hands.
David Taylor: Lighting Designer and Consultant UK and USA

From Dentistry to Lighting Design

My time at university, getting a dental degree, was really spent doing shows with the operatic society. There was no time for anything else as the degree course was 50 weeks a year during the clinical phase.

When I moved to Bingley in '78 and joined Bingley Little Theatre it was primarily as an actor and a singer. Two years passed, and I expressed an interest in lighting. There was a vacancy for the next play so I was pushed in at the deep end and rapidly started to learn what type of lamps there were as well as starting to acquire a knowledge of gel colour.

It seemed as time went on that the process of lighting plays became more enjoyable than the act of being in them. The thought processes involved with creating the required effect with the least amount of expense became a challenge which I enjoyed far more than the routine learning of lines.

There is something intensely gratifying when a box set comes to life with shadows in corners and the flickering of a fire, or perhaps a black box where the sun can rise from one side of the stage and set on the other or the wooded glade with a gentle gobo wash covering the cast. One of my favourites was the underwater sequence when dancers became crabs and rocks dappled with moving patterns against a graduated sea-green cyc.

Of course it is not always easy nor is it always right first time. How long is that fade time? Can we not just tweak it that little bit? Much easier today with memory desks, but *Wuthering Heights* was fun with 176 cues on a manual desk!

Would I do it again? YES.

Have I had fun? YES

Would I encourage anyone to have a go? ABSOLUTELY YES.

Standard or custom gobos tie the lighting completely into the projection to create a single visual world in which you can't see where one element ends and the other begins.
Katherine Williams: Lighting Designer UK

- Always do a colour test for gel against paint for flats or wallpaper This can either enhance a set designers hard work or ruin it
- Don't over colour, can get a brown mush if not careful
- Do remove all switches from practicals, table lamps, wall lights etc, you can guarantee that your cast will turn them off but never on
- Read the script then "Ah what light at ..." might happen in the right place rather than not
- Don't bring up the fire effect until after the match has been struck Lightning before thunder
- Think of the period of the piece, interiors by candle light are different to those with fluorescent tubes
- The sun rises in the East and sets in the West
- If there are a lot of practicals will you run out of circuits, if so a bit of planning can get you out of trouble
- Do not get stuck in a rut, experiment with colour, get that new gel
- Try to use a special more than once then it was worthwhile all that rig time, two jobs good, three jobs better

Richard Thompson

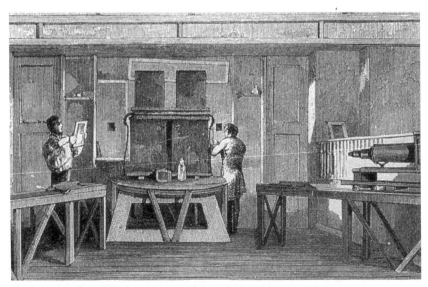

Track mounted magic lanterns enable variable image sizes.

Short Basic Guide to Lighting Design

Why?
Enhance the set
Focus Attention
Set the Mood
Back the story line

When?
For effect
To reinforce
To hide or highlight part of the stage.

What?
The stage
The audience
The actors

Types of Lighting
Direction – front, side, top, back
Tools – Lanterns (Flood, Profile, Fresnel, PC), dimmers and colour system, colour filters, gobos, special effects, (smoke, strobes etc).

The Set Up
Read the script
Listen to any music that goes with the play
Note times of day/ night action take place
Look for author notes, note any special effects
Note any practicals

Meetings
Talk to the director as you are there to assist him/her
Talk to the set and costume designer as they are equal part of the design team
Talk to your crew

Rehearsals

Go to as many rehearsals as you can
Make notes on timings
Make notes on 'blocking'
Make notes on set layouts
Start to think about a style

Start to Design

Make a list of the resources that you have (equipment). Decide on the feel of lighting that suits the play/show.
List any type of special effect (smoke, strobes etc)
Use of colour
Types of focus
Angles of light

Things to Keep in Mind

Limitations of the venue
Limitations of the equipment
Limitations of the crew
Limitations of time
What about another rehearsal?!

Start to Draw Out Your Design

Remember 'nothing is engraved in stone'.
Remember any directions that you have been given by the director
Look over your notes
Start with the general coverage then the specials
List any colours and gobos that you may need
List circuit numbers you are going to use (dimmers)
Remember this is the time to list all the practicals and special effects that will be used on the play/show.
Remember keep it as simple as you can.

Time has Come to Rig

After you have talked your design through with the director and the other designers and all is well the time has come to rig.
Rigging the lights normally happens before the set goes up.
Focusing of the lights normally happens after the set has gone up.

When you focus, this is the time for you to gel up and rig any gobos, special effects and practicals.

Plotting

Through your preparation you should set down to the plotting and have a good idea of how many cues you have.

Through going to rehearsals you should have a feel for the pace of the play/show and in turn you should have a feel for the times that your cues will have.

Time

Allocate your time carefully, set basic coverage states first.

Golden Rule

It is better to have a few good lighting states rather than many bad ones.

Tech Run Through

Check your light levels, the times, the actors are lit.

Be decisive, people will look to you for leadership.

The start of the end of your job.

If something is not working this is the time to change it.

The director should be there for you.

The Dress Rehearsal

The last time you will have to make sure it looks right.

You may need to take out cues or special effects if they are not working.

At this stage try to keep changes to a minimum.

It is not uncommon for it all to go wrong during a dress run.

DON'T PANIC.

The First Night

Let your crew get on with it.

Enjoy the show.

At this point if it goes wrong then it goes wrong.

Take your bow and afterwards thank your crew.

Paul de Ville

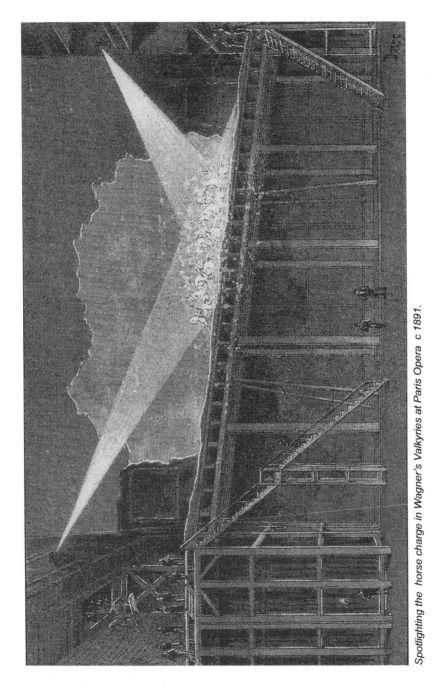

Spotlighting the horse charge in Wagner's Valkyries at Paris Opera c 1891.

Imaginative Lighting on a Budget

My work experience was as an Engineering Manager with BBC TV Outside Broadcasts where I have organised live Outside Broadcasts from a cross channel ferry, a catamaran in the Solent, a steam train, a big dipper, a moving dustcart, an airship, and from the middle of the Channel Tunnel accompanied by Mr. Blobby. I lit the last three years of the original series of Dr. Who, appearing in several episodes both as a press-ganged extra and by accident, and found working on Grange Hill little different from my weekends spent helping run a local Youth Theatre where I train the young technicians. But in both incarnations I have to deal with producers whose aspirations far exceed their budget!

Riverside Youth Theatre is based in an Arts Centre in Sunbury, and some of the lights still in use would delight historians of ancient lights – but they still work! The Strand 123s have bigger lenses than their modern equivalent, giving better control of the barn doors. The Strand 45s, which look like a biscuit tin and have no rear reflectors, still make good narrow spots to pick out scenic highlights, and you can patch four of them onto one 2K dimmer channel to splash up a cyclorama for a dance number. So don't throw away working lights.

You may only have 12 or 24 channels available in a venue, but that doesn't mean you can't re-patch lights during the interval. Often you will find that specials are only used in one act, so that's a good way to gain more channels. Why not change gel colours during the interval to ring the changes on dance numbers, for instance? You may think this is an amateur way of working – but that's exactly what they do at the Royal Opera House! There will often be a rehearsal of one opera in the afternoon, with a different performance in the evening. Electricians with plots clamped in their teeth swarm up the ladders and walkways refocusing lamps to a written instruction, changing gels, and replugging – sometimes more impressive than what is about to appear on stage …

There are three main elements to stage lighting. Firstly without light the audience won't see anything. Secondly you can help make the audience believe in the setting on stage. If your actors are indoors in daylight, and walk across to look out of the window, there should be obvious light on their faces from outside, and you can also add a second light positioned over the window to carry the light further across the stage. These could be on the same channel, and if one is too bright just put some diffuser on the front.

The third element is the most interesting, and that is to convey the mood of the action. The tabs open to reveal the inside of a cottage, you can see daylight through a window, and the door to the outside is partly open. A man is hiding behind the door – and then a young girl steps in …

Lets look at two scenarios. He pulls out a knife and creeps up behind her – or he produces a bunch of flowers and says "happy birthday daughter". In the first scenario he should be in shadow, perhaps a streak of light across his face, the cottage should be dark relative to outside, the girl could be backlit as she enters. Secondly sunlight fills the cottage, birds tweet (OK that's sound), and you can see the faces well lit. You as a lighting person are preparing the audience for what is about to happen – putting them in the right mood.

Lateral thinking can help you overcome a lack of equipment and money. The Youth Theatre performed a play set in a space ship, which had to fly through space, and have a screen on which aliens had to appear. We had a cyclorama at the back of the stage, and rigged a white gauze across the stage about three feet in front of it. We then hung an old mirror ball between the two, and distressed it by knocking off some of the segments. By focusing two Strand 23s on the rotating ball, one from each side of the stage, we had four streams of 'meteorites' streaming apparently at random across the cyc and the gauze. It was so realistic I used exactly the same technique to shoot a Dr Who scene with the camera looking over the shoulder of a bus driver flying through space whilst on location in an alleyway at Butlins Holiday Camp in Wales – don't ask!

The video screen was even more cunning. We used a window flat with a gauze stretched across the opening. The "alien" lay on his back behind the flat, head to audience, and we positioned a window frame at 45 degrees behind and above the gauze with a neutral density gel smoothed onto the glass. We had a backing behind the window which when lit to match the cyc could be seen straight through the semi-mirror, then as we dimmed the backing and brought up a tight spot on the actor's face the window became a full mirror and a disembodied head appeared spookily in the screen. An experienced lighting man in the audience complained that it wasn't fair that I could borrow high tech equipment from the BBC, and I was delighted to get one of my team to show him two ancient lamps and window "liberated" from the council tip!

> I carry a swatch book around in my head. As I see, feel and respond to colour and colour combinations in the real world, I make mental notes of the colours I see and my responses to them. I have a storehouse of emotional and rational responses and the colours that go with them.
> *Gilbert V Hemsley Jr: Lighting Designer USA*

A recent production was the story of the Nativity, and needed a moving star for the wise men to gaze on in wonder. We couldn't afford to hire a moving light, so got hold of a pan and tilt head from a security camera, courtesy of one of the Dads, and mounted our trusty 23 on it with a star gobo. By gently panning the head we could drift the star along the side wall of the auditorium, then fade it out as we ran out of movement.

You don't need banks of lights or stacks of dimmers, you don't need the latest computer controlled consoles, you just need your imagination, your enthusiasm, and the will not to give up when initially you can't see a solution. Let's hope one day someone will say to you "how on earth did you do that" – and you can show them a collection of bits and pieces gathered from back stage and cobbled together to produce a fantastic effect! Good Luck!

Ian Dow

The Legendary Svoboda with the Chromlech Touch

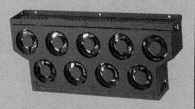

Originally designed by the famous Czech scenographer, Josef Svoboda, this fixture was intended to create dramatic scenery using only light. Its nine low-voltage lamps ensure the traditional Svoboda generates beams of light that are extremely bright, yet soft at the same time. It gives lighting designers the ability to generate light curtains for back-lighting, down-lighting or full front light.

The Svoboda 2.0 from French company Chromlech is a striking combination of this classic fixture and the award-winning Gleamer low-voltage dimmer. The individual control and dimming of each lamp allows a wide range of lighting effects that were previously impossible to achieve, such as three-dimensional chases, individual lamp flashes, alternate pulses, etc.

The Svoboda 2.0 effects can be obtained using a completely new system or, for existing traditional Svoboda fixtures, through the installation of the SV106 retrofit cabling kit. In both cases, the use of the revolutionary Gleamer is necessary.

Gleamer is the first dedicated low-voltage dimmer in existence and the perfect control partner for creative use of Svoboda's unique lighting abilities. In combination, they are highly flexible tools for the creation of custom lighting effects for rock concerts and live events.

Chromlech products are available in the UK through White Light in London.

Drafting a Lighting Plan

Computer Aided Design (CAD)

For many years lighting designers have drawn their lighting plan using computers mainly because making changes and sharing the lighting plan by e mail or via a file sharing application is much easier than with a hand-drawn lighting plan.

Very few lighting designers hand draw lighting plans these days although a few still do and if they have an assistant lighting designer then they get them to copy the hand drawn plan into CAD. For small projects sometimes hand drawing with a stencil is quite and easy.

There are many CAD software packages available but Vectorworks has become an industry standard for theatre with some designers using AutoCAD or WYSIWYG by cast lighting.

Scale & Ground plans

Lighting plans must be drawn to a scale. However you chose to do it, it needs to be done accurately to ensure all equipment fits in the rigging space available without obstructing any pieces of set, masking or other lanterns, speakers, projectors, etc.

A lighting designer must be able to read set ground plans to understand the position and any movement of the set. Accurate measurements should be taken when rigging around set pieces.

A hand-drawn lighting plan needs to be traced over the top of the ground plan. Lighting plans that are hand drawn are first drawn in pencil then inked in when the design is complete.

It is important that they are neat and easy to read. The industry standard for set ground plans and lighting plans is a scale of 1:25 which is often reduced to 1:50 to fit smaller lighting plans onto A3 sheets.

Using CAD the process is the same but each element is on a layer that can be turned on or off in the software so, when printing the final plan, the set layer and any other details can be turned off to show just the basic architecture of the performance space and the rigging positions with lanterns making it easier for the lighting crew to read.

Notation & Key

Each type of lantern should have its own symbol which is usually an exact copy of the top view of the lighting fixture being used.

It may not always be possible to match every lantern when hand drawing but stencils, for hand-drawing, and some CAD software include basic generic symbols of different sizes of fresnels, profiles and pars etc, which can be used instead.

The Key

The symbols should be marked with the lantern type and manufacturer and listed in a key on the right hand side of the lighting plan.

The wattage and the number of each lantern required for the design should also be listed.

Dimmer numbers

Dimmer numbers are generally shown behind the lantern in a circle and if more than one lantern is plugged into a dimmer then a pairing line should be drawn on a hand drawn plan. Most CAD software does not use pairing lines.

Channel numbers (soft patching)

All professional lighting consoles have the ability to choose a channel number and assign it to an output (dimmer) which means that, regardless of what dimmer is powering the lantern, the number typed into the console can be anything the lighting designer wants it to be.

Lighting designers should always try to use they own numbers even in a small venue as this helps to identify fixtures easily and they can develop their own numbering systems that maybe used from production to production.

This can also mean lighting designers spend less time looking at their lighting plan and paperwork and more time looking at the stage as they can start to learn these numbers off by heart.

Soft patching is also essential when touring a production so that the numbers stay the same in every venue where, of course, the dimmers that are powering the lanterns have different numbers.

If a soft patch is used then channel numbers will be shown next to each lantern and dimmer numbers may be in circles.

It is preferable to provide the lighting crew a plan showing only dimmer numbers as this can be clearer to work from.

Colour should be shown in the front of the lantern by number and, if two colours are used, then there should be a minus sign between them. If the colour is split, (i.e. cut in half or quarters) then a '/' symbol can be used.

CAD software varies in how this is done but there is often a way of changing the symbol layout.

Lee and Rosco are the two main manufacturers of colour in the UK and, to differentiate between the two, a hash sign or an R is used in front of any Rosco numbers and an L for Lee filters. If other manufacturers' filters are used such as Gam or Apollo, then some appropriate abbreviation should be used and explained in the key.

Gobo numbers can be placed within the body or at the side of the lantern preceded by a G or the manufacture code. If an Iris is used, an 'I' is placed often in the middle of the lantern body, and is explained in the key.

Booms

Vertical lighting bars (booms) should be drawn accurately to scale on the plan. It is very important to draw the base in the right place, to prevent it interfering with set pieces, trucks or actors' entrances. If the boom was drawn as a vertical line, it may well cut through or interfere with the horizontal lighting bars, making the plan difficult to read, so instead a diagonal line is drawn from the desired position of the base. An alternative way of drawing a boom is to position a vertical line on the plan where it will not interfere with any other bars, then join it to the base with a curved line.

Practicals & Floor lights

Electrical practicals may be marked on the plan using a circle or square to scale appropriate to the size of the practical. This should then be explained in the key or in a notes box which can be presented as an information box under the key.

Any lanterns on floor stands should be marked using the stand symbol on a stencil, again this should be explained in the key.

Title Box

Each lighting plan needs a title box, to give details of information relevant to the show. This should include the following:

1) Show

2) Company

3) Venue

4) Director

5) Designer

6) Lighting Designer

7) Production Electrician

8) Date of Completion

9) Scale

Distributing copies of the lighting plan (file sharing)

When the lighting design is complete copies should be made and distributed to the production manager, head flyman and the production electrician. The flymen or technical manager needs a copy to see which bars are to be used for lighting and to work out the weights required for each bar.

File sharing:

On most productions the Production Electrician or Lighting Designer will setup a DropBox folder and e-mail a link to anyone in the team that needs to view the lighting paperwork and lighting plan.

This means that constant changes can be made by the lighting designer to the plan and everyone has access to the latest version.

DropBox has become the industry standard for file sharing as it is free, works on PC and Mac and means that all the information from show to show is kept safely and can be accessed easily.

If a venue does not have a copy of the CAD software the lighting designer is using to view the plan, it can be saved as a PDF version that anyone can use.

Printing a CAD plan

It is important to have a large format printer than is capable of printing A1 or A2 size copies of the plan as just printing onto A4 is too small to be practical.

A3 printers are inexpensive and may be sufficient for small venues if a scale of 1:50 is used.

Viewing your plan in the space:

Printed A1 or A2 size plans are still good for the lighting crew but lighting designers often prefer to view the plan in pdf format on an iPad (other tablets are available). This is a great way of working with a lighting plan as it is always back lit so there is no need for a torch during a focussing session. It is also easy to zoom in and out and navigate around the plan so there is no longer any need to wrestle with a large piece of paper.

You can e-mail yourself a pdf of your lighting plan and if you make any changes to your design you can just e-mail yourself another updated pdf from your CAD package.

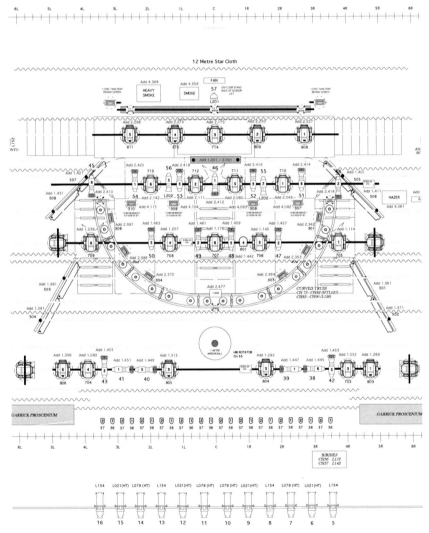

A section of the lighting plan for Respect La Diva, Garrick Theatre 2011, Paul Moorhouse.

The Production Process

Overview

The basic outline and running order for production processes can vary, although the amount of time allocated for each process varies depending on the size of the venue and show. The production manager will draw up a schedule and circulate to all departments to ensure that each department has enough time to carry out their work. The general pattern is as follows:

The Get In

The lighting 'get in' happens first before that of other departments to take advantage of the empty space and gain full access to the lighting rig without any obstruction from set pieces.

The theatre space should be in a state of 'back to black'. This means that the stage and auditorium are completely clear of set and other items and that the walls and floor are free from obstructions and painted black.

The LX team, led by the Production Electrician, is then able to rig the lighting fixtures. Fixtures rigged on booms or floor stands are often rigged after the set get in has been completed as these may obstruct the construction team in their work.

Every fixture is then checked to ensure it is working, has the right colour filter, is plugged into the correct dimmer and ready to focus.

The Set Get In

The next stage of the process, the set get in, can then begin. The construction team will fit up the set and construct any large set elements that cannot be constructed outside of the venue in the workshop.

Time may also be allocated for scenic artists to paint anything that could not be achieved in the workshop or that needs repainting after it has been put into position. The floor will also need to be worked on by the Scenic art department.

The Focusing Session

Once the set is in place the lighting fixtures can all be focussed, normally over a single day or a minimum of two four-hour sessions for a small production. A larger production may need several days for the focusing session.

The lighting designer works with the production electrician and the lighting crew to focus each lamp individually to the desired position. It is important to have quiet and darkness within the theatre space for this to take place. Good communication between the lighting designer and the lighting crew member focussing the lighting fixture is essential.

It may be a straightforward process to get to each lantern but can be time-consuming if the set is complex and fixtures are hard to access. If a lantern cannot be reached at all and is on a fly bar then it can be 'bounced focus' which means flying the bar in, making a small adjustment to the focus and flying the bar out to then see what it looks like.

This session can be long and arduous and, therefore, needs to be well organised.

Plotting

During the plotting session the lighting designer constructs the lighting states that become the cues for the production. The lighting cues are plotted by a lighting board operator (programmer) and the Deputy Stage Manager writes the cues into their prompt copy in pencil so changes can be made at the technical rehearsal.

Both the director and set designer are usually present during these sessions and the Stage Manager and stage crew may be required to carry out scene changes so each scene can be lit with the correct set on stage.

'Walkers' are required on stage for the lighting designer and director to balance light on faces and set intensity levels for each state. Ideally two people should be used so that stage left and right may be balanced or to provide comparison when different areas are lit as part of the same cue. Walkers are invaluable otherwise you will only be lighting a floor and set and not actors!

The Technical rehearsal

The technical rehearsal is where all technical departments deliver their work and all elements for the production are seen and heard together.

There are two ways of running a technical rehearsal:

The first is to run the show in its entirety regardless of whether there are cues in a section or not and then to go over any technical sequences to change and refine things as required.

The second way is a 'cue to cue' technical rehearsal where only the sections where cues occur are 'teched' and sections without cues are skipped. This is the best method if time is short.

Sometimes it is not possible to 'cue to cue' in a technical rehearsal, for example, if actors have quick changes or have to use props on stage throughout the piece. If time allows, a director would rather run the whole play as this gives more time for the actors to rehearse each scene and to interact with any props.

Dress Rehearsals

A dress rehearsal is when the whole show is run as if it was a public performance.

At least two dress rehearsals are usual but sometimes three may be scheduled if time in the production schedule allows. One dress rehearsal is often not enough but may be necessary if time is short or the technical rehearsal has overrun.

The lighting designer may do some subtle re-plotting during this time but the lighting board operator must make changes carefully and always make sure they press "Go" when the DSM calls the cues.

'Notes sessions' from the director take place between dress rehearsals and time is allocated for each department to give technical notes on stage as required.

Opening Night

Unless there is an open dress rehearsal or previews of a production, this will be the first time that an audience will see the production.

Whilst the opening night feels like the finish line, there may be notes and changes still to come and some sections may even need to be re-teched, depending on how the production process went.

The Get Out

This is where all departments work to get the theatre space 'Back to Black'.

Lighting practicals and fixtures must be removed from the set before the construction department can dismantle the set.

All equipment should be cleared and stored away and the theatre space left completely clear ready for the next production.

Matt Prentice

Back up The Show then back up the back up and then back up the back up!

In the late eighties early nineties The English Shakespeare Company existed to take innovative Shakespeare productions anywhere and everywhere in the World. I'd joined the company after the successful Wars of the Roses period and after a tour of *A Comedy of Errors* was re-booked for *A Twelfth Night* with the addition of *Macbeth* later which would then tour as a pair both in the UK and abroad.

Twelfth Night was Michael Pennington's (co-founder of the ESC) directorial debut with the company and was in conception a fine bright comedic production. Michael Bogdanov,the other half of the ESC, was to be the lighting designer on the Show. I was tasked as the facilitator of that design as well as touring it for the first portion of the tour, after which we were to add Michael B's *Macbeth* which had Chris Ellis as LD.

Having previously toured two Bogdanov/Ellis combinations I knew there was a house style to the lighting and tried to fit their standard rig to the *Twelfth Night* that was a departure from the regular house style, the reason being that twice a week we would have a two-show day – matinee and evening different shows with two hours maximum to turn around the set and lighting.

When *Macbeth* was added we employed a very young Rob Halliday as my number two (I'd known Rob from my time with the National Youth Theatre) so between us we got the two shows working from the one flown rig which at the end of the Macbeth production was a triumph of soft patch, hard patch, and a minimal overhead re-gel. Barring centre down lights and pipe ends it was almost a duplicate rig.

As the shows toured in the UK with a hired stage rig and used local FOH we had various master show disks, one with FOH and one without. (In those days it wasn't as easy to tap into house dimmers from a touring desk.) We kept records and discs from all the venues and various desks we met along the way, and I still have the 8" floppy as well as the HD and non HD smaller ones as well as a paper print-out referenced back to the original plans.

Once a show was set for the week it got its own disc, which had FOH if applicable and soft patch data. The ARRI desk allowed us to put two shows and relevant data on one floppy. We thought that we had all bases covered.

That's the background, and now the hook!

Reading Hexagon is a lovely concert platform but in those days presented a real challenge to any proscenium show. The house staff was always magnificent in fitting shows onto to the stage and after three long days we had both shows in place. Due to the challenges of the space it was a week that didn't have any two-show days, so changeovers could be a calm event with time to solve any problems.

The next three weeks were to be a visit to the Chicago Festival where we were to open the proceedings the following week at the Blackstone Theatre so on the Friday I was to fly to Chicago to start the load-in on Sunday evening. Thursday evening was to be a *Macbeth* with a change to *Twelfth Night* Friday then back to *Macbeth* for Saturday.

At 7.31 pm on Thursday a spring storm caused a complete blackout of the Hexagon's power including the safety curtain being deployed. We waited five minutes or so as all the systems come back up, amps dimmers, house power etc. and the show ran along without incident.

After the Show I have a last chat with Rob and the next morning make my way to Heathrow for a flight to Chicago with the Graham Lister (production manager), and Colin LeGendre (carpenter). We had the year before travelled India, Australia, Japan, and Korea in the same roles in advance of the Company.

Rob had a not too difficult day turning back to *Twelfth Night* and was looking forward to an evening operating the show. Hard patch, re-colour and were re-focus done on stage, and after the set was changed all that was needed before supper was a quick flash through all the states to check for errors or kit having been knocked.

It was then that the curse of the *Scottish Play* revealed itself.

The power cut the previous evening had corrupted that week's show disc! No soft Patch, no states, and of course I had all the master discs and paper plot in my briefcase 30,000 ft over the Atlantic. The soft patch was easy enough to reinstate, the cues themselves a little trickier.

What happened next only Rob can confirm but I later heard from him in his understated way that the show was a hairy collection of sub masters and half remembered states with the plan on his lap. As Rob himself said: "And the fun of running it on faders is that the show looked fine, but the cyc got much, much more flamboyant! And it was much more fun running the show that way, though I'm not sure I'd want to do it every night of the week!"

All respect to Rob that neither the audience, apart from a little old lady who objected to the rustling of the plan and reading of the cue sheets, nor the cast were in anyway inconvenienced.

The moral of the tale is that you can never have too many back-ups as long as they are in the right place!

Kevin Fitz-Simons

The Wexford Way

"It's been a few years since I have had to light anything in rep," says Declan Randall. "And the last one was a contemporary dance festival in Johannesburg, so it was with a slightly nervous anticipation that I took on lighting the 60th Anniversary Festival of Wexford Opera."

Lighting in rep is a challenge. A big challenge. But it can also be huge amounts of fun and very rewarding. Wexford Festival Opera was in its 60th year last year and I was thrilled to have been a part of the Wexford experience. They have a "one designer for all three operas" approach which basically translates as "once you enter the building, be prepared to never again see daylight". I jest, of course; there are some windows in the greenroom and the dock door did allow in some daylight…

Lighting three large-scale operas back-to-back can only be done with an immense amount of planning, skill, preparation and a fantastic team that makes it all happen. Wexford has all of this – in surplus. The tech team at the Festival are truly wonderful and supportive, and there is no way that I would have made it out the other end had it not been for them.

The three operas that were mounted last year were "La cour de Celimene", "Maria" and "Gianni di Parigi": three very different operas, each with their own set designs (and designers) and directors. I will do my best to try and relay the experience.

La cour de Celimene

This is a French opera by Ambroise Thomas which had not been performed since its premier in 1855. OK, so I was not going to be able to watch the Met's production at the cinema, but fortunately there was a recording and the music is beautiful.

La Cour, as it came to be known, was directed by Stephen Barlow and designed by Paul Edwards and they had decided to set it in the period that it was actually written for. Paul's designs were wonderful: a truly beautiful stage design. Of course, every element was a lighting designer's worst nightmare, but it was beautiful.

Let's see… the stage was raked in two directions, tilted and lifted. The set was essentially a curved wrap-around wall with a number of entrances in it. Did I mention that the walls were made of green foliage? The floor was a black and white chequer-board pattern. And there was a ceiling. Of course there was. Oh, and for Act II, the entrances were all covered with mirrored doors. But it was beautiful, and I love a challenge.

Act I was the garden, so an exterior scene, and Act II was her bedroom, so an interior scene. Oh, and all of this sat behind a huge gold-leaf picture frame. Since the bulk of the overhead rig was not going to be of much use to me, we rigged some ladders – at different heights to accommodate for the double rake – which allowed me to get light in through all the entrances of the set. The FOH rig consisted of mostly ETC Revolutions and Vari*Lite 3500Qs which helped to give us the shuttering that we needed to be able to get light into the 'picture'. Of course, my flash of inspiration happened too late – what I should have done was designed an over-sized brass 'picture light' and had the bulk of my kit concealed in there, giving the illusion that the light on the wall was doing all the work. (Sigh) Oh well, next time…

Act II was slightly more challenging as once the mirrored doors were in place, I lost the ladders as a lighting position and I had to take great care in placing any other fittings as the sources all reflected in the mirror and would blind some poor unsuspecting opera patron.

Maria

This Polish opera written by Roman Statkowski was given a modern interpretation by director Michael Gieleta and set designer James MacNamara. The piece was set in the Polish Revolution of the 1980s and had a very modern set design, the key elements being eight gauze-clad towers which were built in a forced perspective and would track in and out in different configurations. Other scenic elements were added to help set the location.

The style was very much a stark and bleak setting, almost devoid of colour, the inspiration coming from a series of black and white photographs by Mark Carrot and in fact some of his images were used during the show projected onto the front black gauze by projection designer Andrzej Goulding.

This show was not able to use the ladders as the towers blocked any useful light from them. The bulk of the work was done by the overhead rig which consisted of VL2500 spots and washes and the FOH rig of movers.

The show had several locations, from small dark government offices and dockyards and the streets of Poland to the plush grandeur of the banquet halls for the elite – and to help set the location we were using a Xenon Hardware 7kW large-format projector to do the scenic rear projection work. I ended up strapping a scroller to the front of the projector and this gave us a bit more control of the images and allowed us to help suggest time of day with subtle colour shifts.

Gianni di Parigi

Donizetti seems to like naming operas "someone of somewhere" – Lucia di Lammermoor, Enrico di Borgogna and this one (to mention just a few). I guess if I were a Donizetti opera, perhaps I would be Declan di Jo'burg... The opera, which was performed at Martina Franca in Italy before coming over to Wexford, was directed by Federico Grazzini and designed by Tiziano Santi. The set had to be cut down quite considerably from the Martina Franca version to fit on the stage, but it was still a fair size, it has to be said. It filled the stage almost from wall to wall, leaving just enough space for the performers to get around.

Again, the overhead rig played a big part here, but we were able to squeeze in some booms on each side giving me a chance for some side light which was a big help. The opera has only one location, the Hotel Parigi and all the action takes place over a 24-hour period, which meant sunrises, a sunset and everything in between. I love lighting realistically – it's a great challenge to be able to convince the audience of the time of day but still maintain a certain theatricality that the director required.

Here we were able to use the entire rig which also included a couple of 2.5kW HMI Fresnels with scrollers which helped to punch some 'daylight' into the space.

La Cour

Most of the rehearsals for each opera take place on stage. The first few onstage calls are generally chorus rehearsals, so I used these as opportunities to test looks, colours and angles and to get a feel for what works and what sort of intensities would work for the show. This meant that when we sat in the actual lighting sessions we already had a good sense of what levels would work for us which helped to speed up the process quite a bit. What also proved to be a great help was to sit with the stage manager and peg cue points in the score and chat about the general feel with the director – this meant that in the subsequent rehearsals I could carry on lighting which also saved us heaps of time.

Act II opened with a shadow duel between the two male leads and we ended up using a Fresnel with the lens removed as it gave us the widest beam at the shortest distance with the cleanest shadow and had to be struck really quickly before the cloth flew out.

Maria

Keeping copious notes and taking loads of photos is a big help when working in rep. It means that we all had a record of what things should look like, where they should be focused and so forth. I had started out by planning to have minimal re-focuses between shows, but some of the positions (towers and perches in particular) were really useful and ended up needing a re-focus for each show. As we progressed, we slowly managed to cut down on the number of changes based on what we actually ended up using. We managed to get each turn-around down to a single page spread-sheet which was helpful. Just to add to the complex nature of the show, the borders changed deads during the show, so the lighting bars also had several deads which made for loads of moving light palettes.

We actually went through a couple of different lighting scenarios until we hit upon the right 'language' for Maria which did make for some frantic last minute plotting and note sessions, but what is rep theatre without a little bit of pressure...

We mounted the final images to be projected and then decided to try something. I wanted to use some stage blood and drip it onto the slide. The result would be that it would appear as if the blood was running up the image as opposed to the obvious down, which looked quite eerie indeed. Or it did, until we had a bit of a syringe malfunction... So we cleaned up the mess and decided to save the idea for another show.

Gianni

This one was a little bit easier – I had the DVD from the Martina Franca performance to use as a guide, and we knew what the general lighting story was, so I was able to crack on in the onstage rehearsals and get the basic looks down which meant that the lighting sessions were spent cleaning and making adjustments which was really good. Of course all we did was to add in the broad strokes, the finessing and more subtle moments were added in with the director's input and requirements.

Of course, we did not endear ourselves to the stage management department as all the perfect prop's table locations also happened to be really good boom positions. One of the other advantages of working in rep is as you get to know the rig and what it can do, you find yourself thinking "oh, that will work nicely for Maria" or "that will solve a problem in La Cour" and so each show grows and starts to take shape while you are working on the others. It is quite an organic process and I found having to think about a completely different show every couple of days to be quite refreshing.

La Cour

After a few sessions of each show being on stage for two days at a time, we started to get to one-day sessions for each show and this is where the pressure cranks up a notch or two. By this point we were running each opera and had, for the most part, tech'ed them all so it was time to fine tune and polish which is the part of any design that I enjoy most.

Maria

We would start each session with a focus turn-around and then would tackle any of the bigger notes from the last rehearsal that we were not able to do on top of the rehearsal as it would have meant plunging the stage into impromptu darkness. Then we would run and clean as we go. With Maria, some the changes were fairly drastic as we were adjusting and making radical changes while we were still finding the right language. For the riot scene, we used a bar rigged full of PAR64s which was flown in to a low height to create the effect of car headlights. The units were fitted with a mask made from black foil with a square cut-out which helped to simulate the effect.

Gianni

We would add in an extra cue here or there as the action and cast started to settle in to the piece, tweak and adjust some intensities, change a colour here or there and tweak timing and cue placements. All I can say is that I am grateful that there are such things as tracking consoles – the thought of having to do a repertory season without tracking is just too horrifying for words!

La Cour

A focus turn-over. A few last little tweaks. Check all the cues. Run the final dress rehearsal. Make a few minor changes.

Maria

OK, delete those cues. What about this? Yeah? OK, good. Plot that. A few more notes from the previous run. Give the new cues to the stage manager. Run the final dress rehearsal.

Gianni

Do the focus changes and check the cues. Clean up a little bit of messiness and run the final dress rehearsal. A few notes to do after, but otherwise on track.

La Cour

Focus. Cue check. Put on black tie. Opening night.

Maria

Focus. Make a few more changes. Add a few more cues. Put on black tie. Open.

Gianni

Focus. Cue Check. One last nip and tuck. Put on black tie. Open.

Phew.

Breathe.

That was fun. It really was.

Declan Randall
From ALD's Focus magazine, April/May 2012

Lighting Tech Tips

When I first worked at Glyndebourne in 1978 the resident lighting designer was the brilliant LD Robert Bryan. I was intrigued about the secrets of working quickly in a constant changing opera repertoire. Bob said to me: "Try and make the focus simple and then it's possible the lighting staff will get the focus right every day and your show will always look good." I often remember those wise words and try to keep the rig and the focus simple and easy to understand.

You might be amused by a simple solution that I introduced recently in Florence when I got really frustrated because I couldn't see the floor. I think it's essential to see what your lights are doing. That's easy when you're in a theatre with a steeply raked auditorium but lighting from the stalls that are low can be very frustrating. I have been seen standing on the armrests in some theatres in order to try and see what was going on the floor.

"What are you doing up that ladder," said the director general of the opera company. "Signora," I said, "I'm up here to see what the opera looks like for all of the audience who are not sitting down here!"

If you're working on a dance piece or a musical it's well worth getting the rehearsal room run recorded onto DVD. Then you don't have to manically try and write everything down. It's great for cue meetings, for working out speeds of cues, for the DSM to 'dry tech' giving cues... for rehearsing scene changes to time.

I gather from LD James Smith that recently he was videoing musical numbers in previews and using the recording to give cue notes to the DSM. I remember when I first started using video recording as a notebook – I said to the young choreographer, who was coming to have a meeting with me, "Make sure you get them to record the rehearsal so we can discuss it when we meet." He arrived and said: "They wouldn't let me record the rehearsal because the pianist would have to paid £50, but don't worry, I can dance the entire ballet for you." I was furious and then started to chuckle as I wondered if we should run the ballet in my kitchen or the sitting room or maybe go outside and stage it in the street. Then I could even invite the neighbours! I'm happy to say that the early glitch was sorted out and I had a video of a rehearsal.

Mark Jonathan

First published in ALD Focus magazine

Why Colour Light?

"Colour can support and enhance the work of the actors, their clothes and their scenic environment"
Francis Reid

"To make the audience feel the scream, live the blues or dance with danger."
Jennifer Tipton

How to Choose Colour Filters

There's an increasing diversity of choice from the various manufacturers, and as the number of colours increase, the individual colour names now don't always describe the colour, as was the case in the earlier days of colour filters.

Open White

Open white is the term for the bare stage lantern without a filter. The term 'open white' of course is relative. If it's a tungsten filament lamp, the appearance may seem to be intense white but on dimming may shift through to the warm emotional level of candle or firelight. If mixed sources are used, the whiteness of metal halide lamp will cause the tungsten light to appear markedly yellower or warmer.

Saturated Colours

Saturated colours are the deep blues, reds and greens. Because they are typically 'pure', as much of the rest of the spectrum is filtered out. If the colour is achieved via a

DARK BLUE

Transmission Y% 3.1

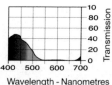

Wavelength - Nanometres

filter, the transmission is low, and much more light energy, i.e. multiple fixtures, are needed to achieve high levels of light.

Deep saturated colours must be used with care for lighting performers and they can distort subtle colours in sets or costumes.

Pastel Colours

Pastel colours are saturated colours that have been diluted with white. Pastels allow a high transmission of light energy, making brighter

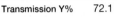
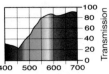

STRAW TINT

Transmission Y%   72.1

Wavelength - Nanometres

final light levels, and make more efficient use of lighting fixtures. Pastels are easier for lighting performer's faces and reveal more colour in costumes and scenery.

Broad Families of Colour

The Whites

There is an increasing use today of colour filters which were originally designed as colour temperature correction filters. They are used to change the light

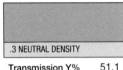

.3 NEUTRAL DENSITY

Transmission Y%   51.1

Wavelength - Nanometres

quality in film, video and photographic use. Lighting designers have also found them attractive as 'effects' colours.

Many filters slightly tint the emergent light from a fixture in a series of finite steps, warming or cooling the source, or in the photographic film world, adding or subtracting 'green' for example.

In this category we can add the Neutral Densities, which are a series of neutral blacks or greys, reducing light but without colour change.

The Reds

Reds are often used in production but rarely with success. They are good for special effects, spectaculars, musical numbers and concerts. They generally

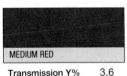
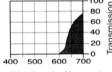

MEDIUM RED

Transmission Y%   3.6

Wavelength - Nanometres

need moderating with more subtle concerts. Deep reds do not work well on faces or on most costume materials. Typical Light Transmission is 4% to 25%.

The Blues

The Blues most probably have the largest range and choice of colour. Almost all blue filters have a small amount of red in them, as the use of pure, cold blue, is rarely desirable.

DEEP BLUE

Transmission Y% 1.1

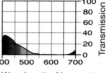

Wavelength - Nanometres

Both the saturated and pastel blues have a range of blue with varying degrees of green or a red component: the first for moonlight and sea visualisation effects and the red dilutions towards purple, magenta and lavender tones.

All the blues are useful for backlight, cycloramas and skies, and for sculpting the human face, for all variation of colours from caucasian to deepest colour tones.

Typical Light Transmission is 0.5% to 50%.

The Greens

Green is one of the three primary colours, and of course, necessary for mixing to produce white light. The green palette runs from very deeply saturated colours

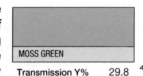

MOSS GREEN

Transmission Y% 29.8

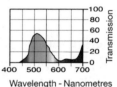

Wavelength - Nanometres

through dilution towards the yellow/green, or towards blue to create rich cyans.

Greens are good for suggesting foliage and pastures, for sunlight and break-up gobos. Greens are also useful as fill light in outdoor scenes and lift shadow areas in moonlight scenes. Green is extremely unflattering to all skintones.

Typical Light Transmission is 7% to 75%.

The colours just discussed are the PRIMARY and SATURATE colours. Now we will review the PASTELS.

The Ambers

The ambers offer a greater choice of colours than the reds and greens together.

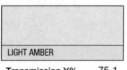

LIGHT AMBER

Transmission Y% 75.1

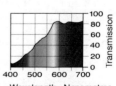

Wavelength - Nanometres

Ambers are a useful group of colours for acting area lighting, and help portray the warmth or the sun or traditional social scenes with artificial sources, firelight, candles, or evening scenes that are emotionally warm in tone.

The pastel ambers are high transmission, pastels are normally safe to use on skin tones, giving warmth without obvious pink suffusion.

Typical Light Transmission is 40 to 78%.

The Pinks

The pinks are similar to ambers, giving warmth, flattering for skin tones, and evening softness through to daylight. Musicals, spectaculars and

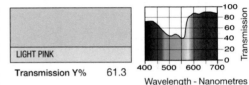

LIGHT PINK
Transmission Y%   61.3

Wavelength - Nanometres

pantomimes are good for the newer vibrant saturated pinks, with a touch of blue.

Typical Light Transmission is 15 to 66%.

The Lavenders

The lavenders are useful because they sit on the fence between warm and cool colours. They can appear complementary to steel blues, light greens, or warm ambers and pinks.

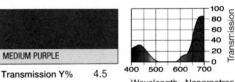

MEDIUM PURPLE
Transmission Y%   4.5

Wavelength - Nanometres

The range includes deeply saturated colours including those mixtures of red and blue proportions giving a variety of lavender, indigo, violet, lilac, fuschia, magenta, mauve and purple.

The pastels are useful for the designer to achieve a clean accent, or highlight the whole stage, or can be used as a modelling side light.

Typical Light Transmission is 4 to 61%.

Other Colours

There are some colours that don't necessarily fall into the above categories.

Yellows are not flattering for skin tones, but they are useful contrast for edge lighting scenery, and as a colour element in 'break up' gobos or lighting foliage.

CHOCOLATE

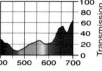

Chocolates are basically, like browns, a yellow diluted with black – good for the darker skin tones.

Transmission Y%   26.4

Wavelength - Nanometres

Clear: present in all ranges, is valuable for scrollers, or for painting on.

Special effects: All the saturated colours can be used effectively to help create emotional atmospheres, from film-noir moonlight, to old night club atmospheres.

Help on the internet

Two manufacturers have excellent websites:

www.leefilters.com

www.rosco.com

Michael Hall, photos: Ken Billington

Lighting Musicians in Churches with no Fixed Lighting Installations

Musicians are usually highly gifted performers. Their range of musical styles and presentation, to express those gifts and to meet their audiences' expectations, varies vastly.

Musicians and Audiences

In terms of lighting requirements, leaving aside the worlds of pop and rock, musicians visiting churches can be loosely divided into three categories:

"We need fixed overhead white light, with clear illumination of our music scores and no light in our eyes."

These are usually classical orchestras and choirs, whose numbers can run into the hundreds, on one stage.

"We need clear illumination of our music scores and no distracting light in our eyes"

These are usually jazz musicians, particularly pianists.

"How many colours have you got and can you light our soloist?"

These are usually folk and show bands. They may bring their own illuminated music stands or ask you to provide illumination.

So, to provide a fixed rig in a church for the whole range of musical styles as I did recently (seven concerts in ten days for the Beccles Festival), on a tight budget, needs careful planning.

Planning the Lighting

Musical Festivals are a rising art form. I was surprised how many times the musicians said: "Oh, you've thought about the lighting; this felt very comfortable to play in," and audience comments included: "We liked the lighting". We are not discussing rocket science, but we must apply ourselves to details. Good church concert lighting is *lots of little things done well.*

First, you must get as much information about the musicians and their needs as possible. Repeated requests to management will find some technical riders filtering down. They will mostly be about sound specifications and the type of organic yoghurt to be provided. But occasionally they specify, for instance, *"four colour washes and solo spots"*, to show that someone has thought about it and they usually include a band lay-out, which can be helpful.

Academy Brass: highlighting a soloist.

There will be nights for which no riders exist. So you should look up the musicians on the web, look at pictures of them performing (if they've posted any) and you can write to the management to ask them about the lighting. This is far better than waiting until they turn up. It shows them you're interested and enables you to give them what they need or to remind them that they are in a church with no blackout and very limited facilities.

Lighting Ambitions Will be Defined by the Following:

Budget, which should be established very early in planning.

Power available, which in St Michael's Church Beccles is 3 x 32 amp single phase, plus some 13 amp points.

Time available: a function of budget, turnaround and artists arrival time to set up.

Lighting positions, which will be all about where stands can be positioned.

Blending musicians' requirements to achieve a common rig with some flexibility.

Architecture. What features has the building, that can be used as decoration and what is best not lit?

For the Beccles Festival we decided to provide two rigs, one for classical musicians and pianists of all sorts and the other for show bands and jazz combos. These were on the same DMX ring and some elements of one rig often augmented the other.

Church Definitions

I will refer to *Upstage, offstage* etc in the normal way but a church orientates itself by the points of the compass and by its traditional areas. So church people will refer to the *East end, the South aisle, the Nave, the Choir.* It is up to you to learn these; Google will provide!

For St Michael's Beccles, our stage was at the East end of the Nave, so *Upstage* was East.

Classical Rig

This is for the "white light overhead and no glare" brigade.

We had to cater for:

> A choir of 110 plus orchestra of 40 plus three solo singers
>
> Two orchestras of 40+ on one night
>
> A brass band of 35+
>
> A concert pianist

A pianist accompanying a semi-staged songs and readings classical recital

The basis of this lighting was 6 tungsten lights, run on 2 x 3-way dimmers off 13 amp plugs. This sounds pathetic but it worked because the lights were Redheads and they were on stands up to 6m high which were in exactly the right positions.

Orchestra scores lit with Redheads.

A Redhead is a film location floodlight, very light and portable, using an 800 watt short-life extra-bright lamp. The light can be modestly spotted by peaking, can be hooded by barndoors and you can clip gels across the outer leaves of the barndoors. They are on some hire companies' stock lists. Their larger 2kW sisters are Blondes!

The stands used for Redheads are again from

Orchestra lit with Redheads.

the world of film location. Manfrotto make a very good range. The ones that I use have a minimum of four sections: '4-lift' and some have six sections: '6-lift'. With these you can get the light over the musician's heads and on to the scores without shedding glare onto the musicians opposite. In churches with temporary stages you will find annoying changes of floor or stage level, which can often be overcome if your stand has a lazy leg; a leg that is extendible.

Lazy leg in operation.

The technique is to start from the back of the stage, which in this case was 32 Steeldeck sections, including some choir risers. Install two of the tallest stands at the extreme corners of the rear stage and pre-tilt the Redheads so that they point down a good way. Arrange the barndoor to shield light from the audience. You have to do this before you raise the stand, unless you have a six metre ladder, in which case you probably don't need stands! At first it's a long case of trial and error but you will eventually get good at it. Glare across the stage is usually fine but should be kept from the audience.

The two mid-stage side stands have the same sort of technique applied as the up-stage ones. If they can be stood next to or anchored to a stone pillar they will be least in the way.

The down-stage pair has to be the most accurately set, as they must not glare into the eyes of the musicians opposite, so the top barndoor must be set as well as the downstage leaf.

For the conductors' scores and any soloists I used elements of my band rig to touch in the areas carefully. At Beccles, the conductors were crosslit with two Brio profiles and soloists were picked out with two 500W wide Par 64 (CP88 lamp), which have a 'letterbox' beam when angled well.

The soloists were also back/side lit with a 1kW very wide Par 64 (CP95 lamp), which I would later use with a colour in it for

100 choral singers, orchestra, soloists and conductor.

the band rig. So their scores were really well lit and they stood out from the choir.

All lights were in open white except for the conductors' specials which were coloured with Lee 151. As many of the singers and orchestra were in *penguin dress* (black and white dinner jackets and best frocks), their faces naturally looked warm in contrast, so white light was fine.

Light from the sides works well for classical musicians as they are either facing inward to centre stage so their music needs lighting, or they are facing front and don't want front light in their eyes.

Piano Lighting

Particular attention had to be paid to the lighting of the piano keys for the solo piano recital and for the song recital accompanist. Both pianists needed constant white light on their keyboard and their score at all times. So I asked them to sit and play, observed the slim angle available between their body and the keyboard and positioned Redheads on tall stands accordingly, as far behind the pianist as possible, to light the keyboard and the score. That meant a well-barndoored and spotted Redhead on a tall stand on stage, which was not intrusive. The pianist was backlit as well as the keyboard and there was no glare in the audience.

Martin Roscoe: keyboard lit with two high Redheads.

The front piano light stand was further on stage than was ideal but very few people had a restricted view and certainly no-one complained. I set and agreed the light levels with the pianists, using the local faders on the three-way dimmers, so there was no possibility of me disturbing the setting when changing the rest of the stage lighting for the readings and the singing.

Houselights

For most of the classical concerts we left the Nave (auditorium) lights on at the sides of the stage but the fitting over the stage was turned off. This is a particularly un-lovely but very efficient double circle of shaded compact florescent lamps which would have drawn the audience's eyes and made everything else dim and indistinct.

If the audience had libretti or programme notes to read we left other lights on at the West end, behind the audience.

Generally, the more colourful and freer the lighting, the less auditorium light was kept lit.

Colour Lighting Rig

This is for the four-colour and specials requirement of jazz and show bands. We had to cater for:

A 1920s-1940s 15 piece period band

A contempory jazz piano trio

The semi-staged classical songs and readings recital referred to above

Some lunchtime 'open mic' and afro drumming sessions

This lighting was provided by 22 Par 64 lights and two Brio profiles, plus Redheads for specific requirements like the accompanist pianist mentioned above. They were powered by 18 ways of Pulsar dimming, which has local control. The upstage lights were generally paired across. Each downstage light had its own dimmer.

Piccadilly Dance Orchestra: colour lighting.

The rig was divided into four long Bi-lite T bars, each with six lights on it. Each T bar was raised by a 3-lift wind-up Manfrotto stand. Two stands were positioned at the downstage corners, just off-stage and two about mid-stage, on the stage

Joe Stilgoe, colours plus Redheads on the keyboard.

so they could be pushed into position as required. These four stands all had *lazy legs*, which meant that the up-stage pair could be positioned on the risers and the down-stage pair could juggle round the church floor.

My comments about side lighting for classical musicians also stand for jazz and bands. The side angles pick out soloists in a dramatic way and some basic modelling can be achieved.

As the Festival unfolded, I found myself using strong colours from the rear bars to light the church *screen*, which is a permanent, wooden, unpainted, open latticed and nicely decorative five metre high divider, which is immediately behind the rear of the stage. I also used some of these mid-stage lights to back-light the bands or soloists.

The front bars, besides the classical highlighting of conductors and soloists, were used for colour washes and for filling in side light.

At one stage I was planning to hire some LED Par 64s for colour variation but it was soon clear that the budget wouldn't allow this. However, we did use some LEDs; my new 'get-out-of-jail' light is a twin-stalk battery powered, 4 LED clip-light. Two of them will light a spread score on a 9ft Steinway and one will be fine for a jazz drummer. Immense value at £10 for the three and that's a sale, not a hire!

Lighting Control

The rig was all controlled by a 24 way Zero88 Jester from the back of the audience. By resetting the DMX addresses on individual dimmer racks, I was able to also leave lighting available for the lunchtimes, when there was lots of daylight in the church but some ambience was needed to stimulate the performers. In these cases the churchwarden could bring up a master lever of an ARRI 12 way preset desk near the stage. Sometimes I left white lighting, sometimes colours.

For the evening concerts the Jester was used in sub master mode, so the

It's evening on Catfish Row and I wanted a clear clean light, but one that said 'night' and illuminated the gamblers. I used a deep blue filter to make the people and the scenery pop. It mixed well with the other colours I used for that warm, sunset glow.
Ken Billington: Lighting Designer USA and UK

colours and areas were easily to hand. I then enjoyed the music and cross faded the masters or touched in specials as the musicians and the mood required.

Running the Show

Although you may not have seen the show beforehand, it is vital that you enter its world and it is essential that you are given a programme. If not, ask for one and don't pay for it; you are part of the performance! Frequently the notes in programmes tell you what is likely to happen next and they give you the shape of the evening. You will avoid peaking early!

At the start of the interval, I always ask the principle musicians if they are happy. Again, it is better to know whilst you have time to correct.

Final Notes on a Niche Lighting Job

What I have described could be called simplistic and unadventurous. But it stems from this key thought: you are lighting a show for the musicians to entertain the audience. Your job is to enhance that and only to embellish it to a point which is not intrusive or distracting. If you want to flash lights, ask the musicians first. But earn the right to do that by getting the basics right first.

It is my experience that there is a lack of good lighting support for small scale musical concerts and this would be a great potential growth area for the many young lighting designers and production electricians now emerging, providing the funds are there to pay for their time. The equipment needed is modest; the stands are the most expensive part.

But the essentials to succeed include a love of some music and a sympathy with all music. If you have that, you will want to see *lots of little things done well.*

James Laws

It is a wonderfully juicy thing to 'paint' with coloured light - to use light expressionistically - to make the audience feel the scream, live the blues or dance with danger.
Jennifer Tipton: Lighting Designer USA

Tips for Lighting Theatre-in-the-Round

Theatre-in-the-round can be challenging, but also extremely rewarding. However, once used to designing 'in-the-round', moving back to proscenium stages often requires considerable readjustment. Theatre-in-the-round is a very natural staging format, and a return to the proscenium format can seem somewhat false. However, theatre-in-the-round offers plenty of opportunity for good fun lighting as well as pure naturalism.

Designing General Cover

Before getting involved in the artistic requirements of a show, the first job is to illuminate the actors wherever they are on the stage. To achieve this, the McCandless 45° rule can be simply adapted to suit viewing positions from all sides, not just the 'front', thus resulting in four luminaires per acting area at a 90 degree separation from each other.

The disadvantage of this method is that it will quickly eat into the resources of the available equipment, leaving the designer with few luminaires and circuits for specials. This situation can become very disheartening to a designer faced with an exciting show, so methods of 'cheating' must be devised to make economic use of the general cover, without compromising on visibility. Cheats can be in the form of fewer angles for general cover, fewer general colour washes, colour washes from fewer angles, variegated colour washes, and the use of devices such as colour changers and remote gobo changers. A typical repertory venue will establish a good all-purpose general cover that is rarely changed, allowing the designers to concentrate their efforts on show-specific design work.

General cover is naturally greedy for a variety of reasons; not least because many theatre-in-the-round venues are generally small and therefore have a very short throw from grid to floor. Short throw requires more luminaires per square foot of stage than a longer throw simply to get a decent wash at head height. More obviously, each stage area needs to be lit with twice as many instruments as the McCandless rule allows, thus doubling the size of the rig to produce the same result.

Two Cover, or Not Two Cover ...

The solution to this question is partially answered by how you would normally work if the production were to be presented in a proscenium theatre. Does the show require two or more colour washes, or is one wash plus specials adequate?

During seven years at the Stephen Joseph Theatre, I only used a true two colour wash once (one at 90°, one at 120°), but often managed to cheat the rig so that it appeared to have more than one colour wash.

It is easy to define 'general cover', and it is easy to define 'specials'. However, my 'pseudo-two colour' rigs comprised a general rig plus specials, plus what I came to call 'cross-wash'.

The cross-wash was in addition to the general cover, but only lit the acting area from one side. A rig might contain two or three of these 'cross-washes' that would be used on top of general cover to add some stronger colours, or in contrast with each other. This results in an interesting and versatile rig, and manages to break a couple of Stephen Joseph's basic rules: the use of colour, and the use of single-sided illumination.

> "It is not usual to fit colour filters to spotlights to the extent that is common practice for proscenium stage work ... of course colour may be used ... but the main scheme will not depend upon it."

Using one or two contrasting coloured cross-washes provides great potential for actor modelling, which can be lacking when a single colour general rig is used. The coloured cross-washes add depth and atmosphere to the general lighting.

> "Single [sided] spotlights are seldom used ..."

Using a strong single sided keylight also helps with actor and settings modelling, as well as other lighting essentials such as time of day and location. The most interesting plays for lighting in-the-round are those that are set outdoors over a duration of 12 or 24 hours. To achieve the right effect, the direction of keylight must be constantly changing throughout the show, which not only tells the time, but is also essential from the audience point of view. It is possible to create some very theatrical, dramatic, or even beautiful stage pictures with lighting in theatre-in-the-round, but this is useless if only a quarter of the audience get to see it for two hours. I always tried to change the direction of the keylight in each scene, both for the benefit of the audience, and as a design challenge.

What is Keylight in-the-round?

Part of the lighting designer's brief is to create an atmosphere appropriate to the setting. The very nature of theatre-in-the-round is that there is often little or no setting at all, so the lighting designer must create the setting itself as well as the atmosphere. This is actually advantageous because you end up with total control over directional lighting, so you can ensure that you can make maximum use of available rigging angles and change the direction of the keylight several times during the show. If you have to light a set where the (virtual) windows, doors, and light fittings are all on the same side, you have a battle on your hands to ensure a good lighting balance all through the show.

In this context, keylight is cross washes, practicals cover, sun or moonlight key and windows, which will often consist of gobos projected across the floor, and also the more obvious specials such as soliloquy spots, set highlights, and anything built into the set or the fabric of the auditorium itself. If the script refers to light fittings, it is worth liaising with the set designer early on to ensure that the fittings are placed in the most useful positions.

Strong directional light can be wonderful for modelling and creating atmospheres but it is essential to view these scenes from all sides of the auditorium during rehearsals. A strong keylight will work well when viewed from either of the sides. When viewed from the same angle as the key, or from the opposite side, the key will look less pleasing. The 'front' may well look too bright and the 'back' too dark, but with excessive modelling over the heads and shoulders. If the scene is short, strong balances like this are perfectly acceptable, but if the scene is longer – maybe the whole act – the lighting must be changed during the course of the scene to alleviate eye fatigue on the dark side. If it is not possible to change the direction of the keylight, for example by an actor turning on another light fitting, then these problems can be eased by slow and subtle follow-on cues. You can make the scene setting statement with a strong key, but follow it up with a

Using a practical (and its reflection) as keylight.

slow build of the general wash after a few minutes. If the fade time is long enough, the audience will not notice the change at all, whereas they would notice the eye fatigue if this measure was not taken. Good team work with the set designer can prevent these types of problems from occurring in the first place.

The best opportunity for the lighting designer to vary the keylight direction is a show that has many short scenes and allows the lighting balance to change continuously throughout the performance. The formula is simple: position the key light sources in as many different places on the setting as possible. A piece located centre-stage will require light emanating outwards, and light fittings positioned at the edges of the stage or 'windows' will require a one-sided wash lighting across the width of the stage. The further this wash spreads, the more useful it becomes. Although small pools of light are often more realistic, it can become distracting if the audience are constantly aware of actors moving in and out of light.

Effects, Pyrotechnics and Smoke

It is possible to use any of the standard special effects that are used in proscenium theatres provided there are suitable routes for cables and pipes, and that all necessary safety precautions are adhered to. Some effects such as UV and dry ice can be particularly effective.

When the stage floor itself is the set, tricks with UV and invisible paint can completely transform it – much to the delight of children who having walked across the floor think that they know exactly what it looks like!

Smoke and dry ice can both be very effective but they do have inherent difficulties. Firstly there is the question of transportation and how to get the effect to the stage. Making a small hole for a practical's cable is easy enough, but making a four inch hole for a smoke duct is another matter. Both smoke and dry ice are noisy and this can also be a consideration. Often a smoke effect has to be accompanied by some sort of sound effect just in order to disguise the noise of the smoke machine itself. Once on stage, the behaviour of the smoke is determined by the air-conditioning. It is essential to organise a smoke technical rehearsal with same amount of air-conditioning as will be used during performances. Even then a carefully timed smoke cue can go wrong once there is an audience producing a new set of warm air currents.

Pyrotechnics are by far the most difficult effects to accommodate in theatre-in-the-round because of the proximity of the audience. All safety instructions issued with the effect must be adhered to, but otherwise, if there is somewhere to run the cable and install the pod – use them if required. Once again though, the technical rehearsal must be using realistic air conditioning to establish the effect of a large smoke burst, and then extracting that smoke.

Painting the Stage

As well as the essential task of lighting the performers, the lighting designer working in proscenium has the opportunity of lighting the scenery both for illumination and for atmosphere. The very nature of theatre-in-the-round is to use furniture rather than conventional scenery in straight plays, or even no scenery at all, and to create the settings just with lighting, sound, and props. In many ways these types of shows are by far the best fun for the lighting designer, as you have a free reign with the lighting and do not have to conform to any predetermined conventions presented by the set design. In this case, the stage floor becomes a canvas for the lighting designer and can be used in many ways. However, there are two points to be aware of. A gloss finished floor can be disastrous for gobo projection, and the lighting designer must be aware of what is happening with light beams at head-height as well as what the patterns on the floor look like.

Lighting for Darkness

It is often said that shadows are as important as lighting. There is some opinion that this is a rather pretentious statement, however there is some truth in the idea. One of the lighting designers most difficult tasks is to create an atmosphere of darkness without it being too dark. In this case it does not matter what staging format is used, it is the same problem, and a problem that will arise many times during a lighting designer's career.

With a couple of show examples in mind, I have concluded that creating dark and/or atmospheric scenes in theatre-in-the-round is actually easier than in proscenium situation. The reason for this conclusion is quite simple. In theatre-in-the-round there are more available angles for contrasting cross washes and creating contrast is one of the best ways of giving the impression of darkness.

I will use the Stephen Joseph Theatre production of *Dreams From a Summerhouse* as an example. It is a musical based on the Beauty and the Beast story and is unusual as a production because the set is made entirely of natural materials: trees, branches, leaves, grass, and the time span is all night long.

The script stipulated that during act one it must be very dark, but that the moon soon rises. Act two continued through the night so I was faced with the problem of maintaining a prolonged period of darkness without causing discomfort to the audience. Firstly I cheated by extending the time period from sunset to sunrise, and secondly I made good use of on-stage practicals allowing for 'cross washes' from many different angles and in surprisingly contrasting colours. Nonetheless, the overall atmosphere still had to be one of 'outdoor night' which raises the age old question of 'what colour is night?'

The question of course is really nonsense – there is no colour. Moonlight is extremely directional and therefore shadowy, but moonlight is merely reflected sunlight so the answer is that night is the same 'colour' as day, only darker. (This theory was formulated after walking the length of Scarborough sea front during a full moon!) However, the average audience readily accepts the use of dark blue lighting as a suggestion of night but there is a technical reason as well as a psychological one for using deep blues. At night, or in other dark situations, the human eye switches from colour to monochrome vision. Using a dark colour helps to kill other pigments and to force black and white vision. So deep blues were used for this purpose. The actual colours used were chosen for two good reasons. Supergel #68 is particularly good for dusk and blends well into night or day, so it was ideal for a time span of dusk 'til dawn, and Supergel #74 was

used as the deep blue. There were many possible choices from the swatchbook but #74 happened to react very well with the material of Belle's dress (Belle being the beauty).

On top of this, there were four basic cross washes plus specials. Roughly speaking, the four washes were keyed from the four corners of the rig in different colours for different purposes, and this resulted in a remarkably symmetrical looking rig plan due to the diagonal repetition of the cross-washes.

Corner one was the moonlight key, predominantly Lee 161 (slate blue) cutting through the darker blues. Corner two was Supergel #21 (golden amber) for a late sunset feel, although this keylight was changed

Keeping a face lit during a dark scene.

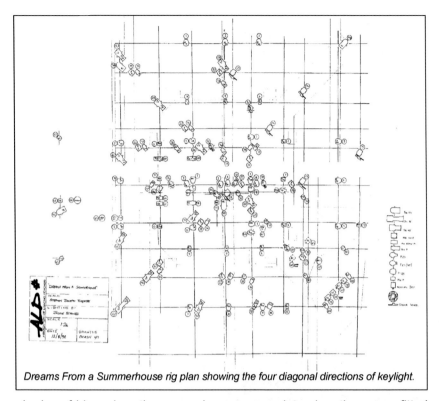

Dreams From a Summerhouse rig plan showing the four diagonal directions of keylight.

shades of blue when the moon rise cue came into play; they were fitted with colour wheels that were also used in another show in that season's repertoire. Corner three was mainly Lee 147 (apricot) as practicals cover for the summerhouse lights. Corner four was not used until the end of the show when the sun began to rise. This was in salmon pinks. There were in fact other practicals on this side of the stage so there was some more 147 to be used before the sunrise.

This formula worked well because the deep blues definitely gave the impression of darkness, but because the four different crosswashes were inconstant use, and constantly changing (lots of 10 and 20 minute fades going on), in terms of illumination the stage was actually quite bright.

More importantly the source and strength of keylight was always changing subtly throughout the show in order to prevent eye fatigue, which can be a problem in long dark scenes.

Extracts from Lighting Techniques for Theatre in the Round,
Jackie Staines, *Entertainment Technology Press.*

Endeavour to Push an Idea to its Purest Form . . .

There can be nothing more beautiful than the light passing through the trees of a summer woodland, early in the morning when the dew is rising as mist and we see the extraordinary light carved out of the woody shade.

Recently I came across a charcoal burner working in a glade in one of our local woods; the smoke from his work was caught in the light and created an image so dramatic it made you want to weep.

The high windows in New York's Grand Central Station casting beams of light across the hurrying commuters.

All these scenes give real life a heightened quality; a theatricality we strive for. Our tool to recreate this in the theatre is the gobo. Gobos can be used to create images of equal grandeur and splendour as those I talk about BUT . . . too often they become a terrible theatrical shorthand. The light in a cobbled street is not cobbled - the surface the light hits is! What is interesting about the light coming from water is that it is reflected, soft, mottled. I don't negate the use of gobos in creating these effects - I just don't often find that they are really the answer.

In lighting what interests me is trying to push an idea to its purest form while still maintaining the performance. Try to take an idea back to its essential form. What happens if you actually bounce light off water? If the light passing through an object is beautiful then try to pass it through that object! Put a tree or a window on stage!

Obviously this isn't always possible. But gobos, while fantastic and a useful tool, can make us lazy in our ideas. Use them when they are the right thing to use, but always think about them, in fact any light in a show, with good rigorous thinking.

Paule Constable
Lighting designer: theatre, opera, dance

Fig 85 Electric switchboard below the stage of the Paris opera, 1887. L'Illustration, (Paris), 18 June 1887, p. 433.

Using Gobos

I use gobos in five distinct ways:
To break up stage lighting into dapples or geometric patterns
A connection between the light source or lighting rig architecture to splinter the beams and create a contrasting physical effect visible in haze.
To create ripples of light as textures move across our audiences
To tranform scenic or architectural surfaces into something unnatural.
Create beams in the air around and about the audience to draw them into our world.

Durham Marenghi
Lighting designer: theatre, concert and television including the
Diamond Jubilee Concert at Buckingham Palace
(*Lighting the Diamond Jubilee Concert* is also published by Entertainment Technology Press)

American Overview:
What is a Lighting Designer?

That seems clear to me but many people have no idea what I do. My mother was impressed that I made shows "very pretty," but she remained fuzzy about how I accomplished my work. So, what are lighting designers and where did they come from? I realise that I offer only an American point-of-view, but I trust that my perspective resonates on both sides of the Atlantic.

Hundreds of years ago there must have been a guy who looked after the theatrical candles and put them out before the stage caught fire. Even then there were maintenance costs: cutting wicks, replacing the gutted candle. He wasn't a designer, however; he was just the candle guy. Then one day, without thinking, he put his glass of wine in front of the candle and changed the colour of the light. But he was still just the candle guy.

When gaslight replaced candlelight, however, the nature and look of the theatre rapidly changed. The man in charge was called the Gas Man, but he was usually a plumber by day and figured out the gas for the playhouse at night. If he didn't burn the place down, he was asked back.

When electricity arrived, the gasman gave way to the electrician. All that sparking energy was an undeveloped science, and the guy who could splice wires and get the lamp to light was looked upon either as a genius or a fool for risking electrocution every time he handled a wire. Sockets were made of wood, switches mounted on wood, and wires tied together, recklessly or cautiously. There were no regulations.

The great American director

David Belasco (1853-1931), author of *The Girl of the Golden West* and *Madame Butterfly*, plays that gave Puccini two great operas, was a perfectionist of realism and theatrical effect. Belasco was obsessed with the effects of lighting on stage and hired Louis Hartman, a technician, to oversee the lighting for his productions. In *The Theatre Through the Stage Door* (1919), Belasco declared, "Lights are to drama what music is to the lyrics of a song. No other factor that enters into the production of a play is so effective in conveying its moods and feeling. They are as essential to every work of dramatic art as blood is to life."

When Hartman started with Belasco in 1901, his program credit read: "Electrical effects by Louis Hartman." For the first time an individual, other than God, received credit as a creator of light. Hartman quickly grew tired of the limited effects of footlights, borderlights, and a few floods. The largest lamp at the time operated with a carbon filament, 32 Watt bulb, a dim intensity at best. Electricity eliminated the old limelight; arc lights offered more economical operation and took up less room backstage.

Belasco hated the hiss and sputter of the brighter arc lights that he had installed on the tormenters and bridges and resented paying the 20 men to operate them. The two weeks of lighting rehearsals also bit into Belasco's budget; without any means communication other than shouting, the operators had to memorise all their cues. Pushed by Belasco to come up with an arc light replacement, Hartman assembled pieces of various instruments at hand, added a baby lens, and put in a concentrated 60v 32w filament bulb[1]. When he finished, he had invented both the incandescent spotlight and modern stage lighting!

So, for the time, lighting remained the electrician's fiefdom. Of course, prominent producers and directors of the time often had a designated staff electrician to light all of their productions. Scenic designers began to consult with their electricians to plan the colors in their spotlights.

When *Trick for Trick* opened on Broadway in 1932, however, its programmes credited a new position, something called "a lighting designer." Abe Feder had come up with the designation and insisted on its use. He later changed his program credit to "Lighting by Feder," and if you examine the recordings of the original My Fair Lady or Camelot, you will see his name listed as part of Lerner and Lowe's creative staff.

Thanks to Feder, our young profession finally had a name, but lighting designers still battled for recognition. Some directors wanted a separate designer for lights, but producers balked at paying a designer to do what the electrician already seemed to be doing. With the New York production

1 Hartman, Louis, Theatre Lighting, Chapter 2, Page 23, D. Appleton and Company, New York, 1930.

of *Medea* in 1947, Peggy Clark became the first lighting designer to get her name on a poster, billed below Judith Anderson and John Gielgud, but billed. Her recognition caused a stir, of course. Stagehands were men, and the electrician was a man, and here was a woman lighting a show, a job that had always been handled by men. When I was 18 and just starting out, Peggy Clark told me that when she went out of town for the pre-Broadway tryout of *Brigadoon* in 1947, the local crew would not permit her to stand on stage and direct the focus. Undaunted and practical, she stood in the mezzanine (dress circle) and shouted her directions to the show electrician, who then passed the information on to a local stagehand who stood on the ladder and made the adjustments. Twelve years later, the great American designer Jean Rosenthal was lighting the original 1959 production of *The Sound of Music*. The producer's head electrician George Gebhardt, who had won a 1947 Tony Award for stage technician of the year, a category that no longer exists, questioned Jean's inventory of equipment and added an extra truck of expensive lights for the out of town tryout. He was certain that Jean would be fired, and he could save the day with all of the extra equipment he had ordered. Jean Rosenthal's work was, as always, impeccable, and the era of the electrician as designer on Broadway finally ended. Art is art, but no producer can bear waste.

Thanks to the folks who fought our early battles, we are now known and accepted as "Lighting Designers", but with the extraordinary advances in technology in the last twenty years, are we better off for it? Belasco thrilled his audiences at the turn of the 20th century, but his actors and his painted scenery languished in dim shadows compared to what we offer today. Over a century after Louis Hartman's heyday, the Broadway and West End audiences expect not just lighting, but the art of illumination. Every theatregoer has a dimmer switch at home in the dining room, and the expectations of sophistication in theatrical lighting increases with each show and each innovation.

Lighting design in the United States uses the more efficient 110 volts, while most of the world uses the larger, 220 volts. Up until the later half of the 20th century, this enabled the American lighting equipment to be brighter, permitting designers to use more saturated colour. Of course, the UK has the Yanks beat in control and dimmers. For a long time direct current, instead of the standard alternating current, limited us to the use of resistance dimmers; we were unable to make use of tubes, electronics, SCR or auto-transformer dimmers. This remained the case until 1975, when Tharon Musser installed the first memory console and SCR dimmers for *A Chorus Line*, and the Shubert Theatre had to replace direct current with alternating current. Broadway was finally catching up with the rest of the world. With the now universally accepted Electronic Theatre Controls Source Four and Vari-Lite automated fixtures the same lights can be used all over the world, and voltage makes less of a difference. We are becoming one lighting world.

Today we start with good, bright equipment and first class computer control, and add all the new toys: colour changers, gobo rotators, light curtains, and so on. I am sometimes depressed to see that many young and not so young designers rely on what I call the supermarket sweep; they order masses of equipment and then figure out what to do with it, as if having one of everything enables you do anything the director wants. This, of course, is not true. You need to layout the show according to the concept you develop after conferring with the director, choreographer, scenic and costume designers, and after considering your space, budget and staff limits.

There is no other field that I know of that holds creative collaboration as high as we do in the theatre. Creating a strong unified vision of the show from the entire creative staff is paramount in achieving a success. If the audience leaves the theatre whistling the lighting something's very wrong,

and I am sorry to say I have done a few shows like that. The best reaction is to hear the audience come out of the theatre saying that the show was great. If lighting designers can contribute to this, their job was well done. Otherwise, it's back to snuffing candles.

Lighting designers are no longer the babies of theatrical design. We have younger siblings in sound and video projection design. We are growing up, but the art and the challenges are always new. What fun it will be to see how theatre lighting evolves as audiences' perceptions constantly grow more saturated with new media.

Ken Billington

The Eiffel Tower Beacon

You will have noticed the dramatic circulating beacon atop the Eiffel Tower in Paris, and no doubt thought little more about it. In fact, what you see at any one time is one of four identical xenon searchlights, each moving around a 90 degree quadrant, and timed to deceive your eye into believing it's one continuously rotating beam.

This trickery took place in readiness for the millennium ceremonies. Lighting designer Pierre Bideau contacted Paris-based Sky Light with a top secret project idea in 1999. Bideau was already well-acquainted with the Eiffel Tower. In 1985, he provided a wash of 'golden light' provided by 350 ArenaVision fixtures installed inside the steel structure. Now, he was looking for a solution to bring back to life the 'old' beams installed in 1900.

For the new millennium ceremonies, it was necessary to focus the world media on the new face of Paris 'Ville Lumière'. He contacted the French company Blachere Illumination to realise a sparkling dress full of diamonds, and in due course was in touch with Sky Light asking them to study a solution to design a spectacular rotating beacon, despite the presence of multiple radio, television and police antennas protruding from the top of the Tower.

At the Sky Light offices, Jean Marie Leriche and his team studied the problem and hit on the solution of installing a servo controlled system of four synchronised searchlight units able to resist all sorts of weather conditions at an altitude of 320 metres.

After a search of the worldwide inventory of manufacturers of searchlights, no weatherproof rotating beacons could be found, so Sky Light decided to start its own research and development. Luckily, ten years earlier, for the centennial of the Eiffel Tower, Sky Light had designed and manufactured its first STX 4200W servo-controlled xenon searchlight and thanks to its hardware and software knowledge and expertise, now mixed its marine experience with that from the entertainment industry. The main idea was to use the most resistant materials to avoid any rust damage risks and to secure the xenon searchlights against water getting into the fixtures.

The four massively strong xenon searchlight units were mounted horizontally onto a yoke with a ball bearing assembly to provide smooth and accurate panoramic movement without any resulting stress for the beam of light emitted. A 630 millimetre electroformed parabolic dichroïc cold mirror was chosen to achieve a perfect sharp collimated beam (divergence 1.4°). A 5000 Watt xenon bulb was selected due to it short arc gap and 1200-hour lamp life.

To feed the lamp it was necessary to install an electronic power supply unit underneath the rotary yoke base. The rotating AC/DC 170Amp rectifier is fed thanks to a permanent mercury 32Amp contact. A front shutter is controlled to open and close the pencil of light with five vanes driven by five solenoid motors for snap effects. Whilst you are in fact viewing the beam from one standpoint, the opposite units are still rotating as one on their panoramic 90 degree angle. The total weight of each rotating beacon is 650kg.

For 12 years, six hours a day, 365 days a year, the system has worked perfectly – proving to world visitors that "Paris – City of Light" is both a dream and a reality.

John Offord

The gobo rotator was born because when I was lighting Chess in 1986. I needed to have indexing squares of light which could register on a full-stage revolving chess board. Then the 'yoyo' was developed because I needed a door opening effect. Its linear movement also made simple water effects possible.
David Hersey: Lighting Designer UK and USA

An early lightning effect – from the Tim Hatcher Collection

LIGHTING PRODUCTS

Two Milestones in Stage Lighting

Milestone 1:

1953 was a momentous year: Strand Electric was the dominant Stage lighting company in the UK, and in April 1953 they introduced a new lantern, the Patt 23.

According to the Strand Press Release, it was aimed at amateur and little theatres. Little did they know that production would continue until 1968, although they worried that the size of the first batch – 144 units, might prove too ambitious!

It was a mirror spotlight, which was first developed in 1936 and tried out in the London Savoy Theatre. In the US at around this time, the company Kleigl launched their ellipsoidal spot, and they had a great advantage, as GE the lamp company presented a whole new range of small cap-up burning lamps.

The Patt 23 was the first lantern designed for mass production; it was made with a die-cast aluminium body, well ventilated, and hinged at the back for lamp access and cleaning. It was fitted with a 250W round bulb, or a 500W tubular lamp. Inside there were two reflectors, made from anodised aluminium, directing the beam to the gate, accurately, helped by the lamp in a pre-focus holder.

The lantern had a 22 degree beam angle, but over the years, other lenses could be bought, for a range of beam angles, or a Fresnel type stepped lens. There were no beam shaping shutters initially, but a straight edge adjustable mask to shape the beam. There was an external frame for holding colour. In 1953, 'gel' really was gelatine and stayed in the Strand catalogue until 1962 when it was replaced by a 'self-extinguishing' filter, either Cinemoid or Roscolene in the US.

Although the frame kept the 'gel' cool and long-lasting, and the die-cast body dispersed the heat, there were many scorched fingers endured when focusing.

More models were produced, one with a rear handle to enable the use of the Patt 23 as a followspot and there were other changes to improve beam shaping shutters.

So the Patt 23 was a major leap forward and over 800,000 were made. There are still some in use and many restored as display pieces as reminders of this icon in stage lighting.

Milestone 2:

Between 1968 and 1992 there were many small changes and incremental efficiency improvements in stage lighting technology – see Philip Edwards' Stage Lighting Timeline page 104 – but there was a special event to come.

In 1992 David Cunningham in the USA designed and invented a radical new spotlight; it was to be marketed by ETC and named Source Four. Like the Patt 23 in its time, the design had a radical increase of efficiency and was an ellipsoidal reflector spotlight. Its primary features are a tool free lamp adjustment, a rotating shutter barrel – which is interchangeable – and an improved lamp and reflector combination.

Each element of the fixture represents an improvement on existing technology. The reflector is a faceted borosilicate, behind the lamp, and is dichroic, it reflects 95% of visible light, but allows 90% of the infra red or heat energy to pass out the back of the fixture.

The proprietary 575W tungsten lamp has four strands forming the compact filament – hence the brand name Source Four. There have been an extending range of beam angle lenses, from 90° to 10°. The stainless steel shutters are easily adjusted. Of course there is a gobo slot and external colour frame.

The Source Four and its development caught the world's attention; it's to be found in almost every rig globally.

Over three million Source Fours made and delivered, and there is no sign of reduction in demand.

So, two Milestones – the Patt 23 and the Source Four. What and when will be the next milestone?

Michael Hall

A Summary of Light Sources

Summarised by

- Advantages and Disadvantages
- Efficiency – in lumens/watts
- Colour Temperature
- Colour rendering

Advantages and Disadvantages of Light Sources

Tungsten and Tungsten Halogen	
Advantages	**Disadvantages**
Bright white light	Lower efficacy than newer sources
Full output on switching	Limited life
No control gear for mains volt lamps	Some less efficient TH lamps will be unavailable in Europe
Relatively low cost	
Good full spectrum light	
Good colour rendering	
Dimmable	

Linear – Compact (CFL) Fluorescent	
Advantages	Disadvantages
Low running costs	Control gear needed
High efficacies	Bulky construction
Long life – upwards of 24,000 hours	Dimming required
Good to excellent colour rendering	Special ballast

Short Arc Discharge Lamps

Advantages	Disadvantages
Range of Colour Temperature from 3000K to 8500K	Needs control gear
Colour rendering good	Not easily dimmed
Bright very compact source	
Long life lamps	

LEDs

Advantages	Disadvantages
Very long life	High capital cost now, but reducing
Can be dimmed easily	Changing technology may make some installations in need of upgrade
Good colour rendering	
Continuous development in LED technology	
Bigger choices	
Improving colour	

My filter philosophy is simple. Colour can support and enhance the work of actors, their clothes and their scenic environment.
Francis Reid: Lighting Designer and Writer UK

Lantern Types

An Introduction

There are many different types of stage lanterns used in theatre and they all have different applications and control light in different ways.

All lanterns can be moved from side to side (pan) and up and down (tilt).

A hook clamp attached to the yoke allows us to attach the lantern to a lighting bar by means of a threaded wing nut, which can be tightened clamping the lantern securely to the bar.

A secondary means of support must always be attached in the form of a steel wire bond which should be placed round the yoke of a lantern and round the lighting bar.

Lanterns have different intensities due to the many different wattages available. Coloured filters and frosts may be added to a lantern by placing a colour frame into the colour runners on the front of the fixture.

The size and shape of the light beam may be adjusted and the quality of the edge of the beam, soft or hard, may also be adjusted.

All lanterns should be fitted with:

- A 15 amp or 16 amp plug top
- A high temperature silicone cable, called the 'lantern tail', connecting the plug to the lantern
- A hook clamp for attaching the lantern to 48mm scaffolding tubing (Scaff bar)
- A safety bond, rated correctly and tested to the weight of the lantern
- A pan and tilt locking mechanism to direct and secure the lantern into position
- A colour frame for inserting colour filter/frost

Profile Spot

Profile spots are perhaps the most versatile theatre fixture. It is so-called because it can achieve a hard-edged, focused spot. This means that any gobo placed in the gate can be projected as a sharp image.

Profile spots are available as fixed lens or zoom lens units. Zoom lenses can change the size and sharpness of the beam by moving the lens or lenses, instead of the lamp or reflector which remain stationary.

Control of the beam size and shape in a standard profile is achieved by the optical system known as the 'gate' where the beam is shaped by four 'shutters'. The gate of a profile also carries two metal runners that can accept an iris (a mechanical device designed to increase or reduce the beam size) or a gobo (a metal or glass 'mask' or template that projects an etched image when the profile is in hard focus).

The gate can be rotated on most good quality profiles so that the shape formed by the shutters can be aligned in the desired position. This rotation also allows the gobo angle to be adjusted which is very useful, for example, when text is being projected and needs to be precisely aligned.

Flat Fielding a Profile Lantern

Profiles have a knob or screw adjustment on the lamp housing which moves the lamp within the optical system. By adjusted the lamp position, the beam can be 'flat fielded' to distribute the light evenly across the field of light. This is particularly valuable when using glass gobos which can break if the field has a 'hot spot' i.e. an area where the light falls more intensely on its surface.

Fixed Beam Profiles

Fixed beam profiles have only one lens which can be moved to give the beam edge a hard or soft appearance. A range of beam angles are available and must be specified on purchasing. Some of the latest designs of fixed beam profiles have interchangeable lens tubes that can be swapped between fixtures. This makes economic sense as different lens tubes can be fitted to the same body, decreasing the cost of a rig and make the lanterns more flexible.

Zoom profiles

Zoom profiles are extremely versatile as both beam quality and beam angle can be adjusted. This is achieved using two lenses – one adjusts the beam angle and the other the sharpness of the beam. Zoom profiles come in either wide or narrow angle beam sizes and their range of angle depends on

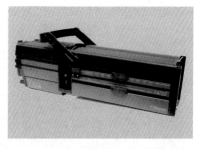

the design of the unit and the manufacturers' specifications. Zooms are appropriate for theatres that are producing a lot of different productions and, therefore, have a rig that will be constantly re-focused or changed.

Cool Beam Profiles

Most manufacturers have their version of a 'cool beam' profile as a result of the development of two new technologies. Firstly, the development of a high performance lamp (HPL) has increased the efficiency of the light source so a 575W lamp now has the brightness of the older 1200W lamps. HPL lamps have a compact-filament halogen (Krypton) gas and the lamp base incorporates a heat sink to dissipate the heat generated from the source.

The second feature of the design is the dichroic reflector which prevents much of the heat from entering the gate of the lantern and thus makes gobos, shutters and colour last longer.

As less power is used for equal brightness these new fixtures are a greener alternative to the older type and over time will save money on expensive electricity bills.

Fresnels

The main characteristic of a Fresnel lantern is its lens. The lens has a distinct appearance that is stepped on one side with a textured surface on the other. This gives a very even field of light and softens the edge of the beam. Because of its soft edge there is no defined point where the light stops, so multiple units can be used to blend well and give a smooth coverage of light.

Barndoors

Barndoors are simple devices made of four flaps of metal that are fixed to the front of a Fresnel lantern. These can be used to shape the beam of light and mask areas, such as the edge of a piece of set or stage area, shielding them from overspill. The barndoor flaps can be rotated to allow almost any angle to be achieved.

Barndoors are also useful for getting rid of any light spill that may be cast from the lens as the light passes through. Older Fresnels always used to come in 500W, 1000W and 2000W units but the newly designed halogen lamps now mean that the units can take 650W, 1200W and 2500W lamps.

PCs (Pebble Convex)

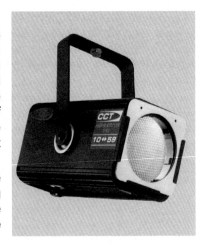

The pebble convex lantern, or PC as it is now known, is of similar design to the Fresnel. The beam size can be adjusted by moving the lamp and reflector while the barn doors give control of the direction of the beam of light. However, unlike the Fresnel, the lens is stippled which refracts the light to give the beam a soft edge.

This soft-edged has a harder edge than the Fresnel which some lighting designers prefer, depending on the application of the lantern and the overall effect required.

The wattages of these lanterns are the same as for Fresnels and are made by a variety of manufacturers.

Plano-Convex (PC)

Confusingly, the Plano-Convex lantern was the original PC. It has a clear lens which gives a hard edge beam similar to that achievable with a profile spot. Its variable zoom, however, gives more coverage per fixture than a zoom profile, and better beam shapes than fixed beam alternatives such as PAR cans.

Lantern Types – Floods

The simplest lantern used in theatre is the flood. A flood is basically a lamp and reflector in a box with no facility to adjust the focus, size or shape of the beam. The spread of the light, and consequently the area covered, is dependent upon the distance between the flood and the object being lit. This can make the flood difficult, or even unsuitable, to use if light needs to be controlled within a tight area.

Floods are used generally for lighting large scenic areas, such as backdrops and cycloramas rather than the acting area where a higher degree of control is needed.

Floods come in different wattages – the most common being 500W and 1000W, with the larger 1000W flood giving a larger beam spread than a 500W.

Linear and asymmetric floods

A linear flood has the lamp mounted in the middle of the lantern so the same amount of light is spread from the top and base of the unit. These are very useful as working lights but are not as good for lighting backdrops as an asymmetric flood and are therefore less common in the theatre.

An asymmetric flood has the lamp offset at one end of the unit so more light is directed out of the opposite end. A large scooped reflector increases the spread of light. This makes these units very useful when lighting a backdrop from the top or the bottom.

Multi Cell Floods (Cyc units)

Multi Cell floods are arranged in banks and used to mix colour on a backdrop or cyclorama cloth.

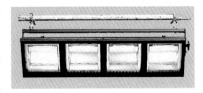

Often referred to as 'cyc lights', these are either 2, 3 4 or 5 cell units which can be placed on the floor or in the rig depending on whether the object is being up lit or down lit. If the units are placed on the floor they can be called 'ground rows' and if they are rigged above are sometimes referred to as 'battens'.

Parcans
Long Nose Par 64

The Parcan is a lantern in which the optical system is built in the lamp, with the lens, reflector and lamp filament all in one unit. This is housed inside a metal body and only the direction of the light can be altered. This makes the optical system very compact and therefore very efficient in turning electrical energy into light.

This high degree of efficiency results in a very white light with a high colour temperature that renders dark colours more visible on stage. Unsurprisingly perhaps, the Parcan originated in the rock & roll industry where its saturated colours proved popular for lighting bands. This factor is also useful for theatre where, for example, dark blues may be used to light a night scene or to add a strong punch of light through a window or door on set.

Par 64 Short Nose (Silver)

The beam of a Parcan differs from other lanterns in that it is an ellipse (oval). This is caused by the linear filament of the lamp which throws more light out in one direction than the other. A Parcan lamp housing, therefore, has the facility to rotate the lamp inside the can so the ellipse may be focused in the required orientation.

Parcans are available in many different wattages and voltages but the most common in British theatre is the 230V 1000W type called a Par 64, available in a long or short nose versions. The four standard lamp sizes are listed below:

CP 60 Narrow

CP 61 medium

CP62 Wide

CP 95 Extra Wide

Because the optical system is built into the lamp, replacement can be very expensive but this is off-set by the fact the cans themselves are relatively cheap.

Birdie (low voltage Par lamp)

A birdie is a scaled down version of a Parcan (the name 'birdie' comes from a golfing term meaning 'one under par') and was originally developed for the display lighting market. A birdie uses a 12V dichroic lamp which, unlike the Parcan, has a central filament and therefore produces a circular beam. Lamps can be a variety of beam angles, the angle determined by the texture of the reflector which diffuses the light.

One advantage of birdies is their size which makes them easy to hide on set or in places where it is difficult to inject light. Another advantage is the low voltage which allows them to run off a 12V battery. This makes them ideal for use in places where a cable would be an obstruction, with control provided via wireless dimming.

230V mains version birdies require no transformer and terminate into a 15amp plug. Like a standard Parcan, birdies come in short or long nose versions and a barn door can be added for more control.

ETC Source Four Par

A Source Four Par, developed and manufactured by ETC Lighting, is modelled on a conventional Parcan but with some major differences. Unconventionally, the lamp base and reflector are built into the body of the lantern with the lens a separate item at the front of the unit. The beam angle is altered by changing the lens to one of the four standard beam widths available. The oval beam is altered by rotating the lens using the adjustment at the front of the lantern.

Like an ordinary Parcan the beam is elliptical, and like the Source Four Profile it uses a 575W or 750W HPL (high performance lamp). A standard Source Four Par has an aluminium reflector, although a cool beam version with a MCM (metal cold mirror) reflector is available.

Matt Prentice

Lighting Equipment Preparation

Lanterns should be inspected and prepared before they are rigged to ensure they are in working order while still at ground level.

PAT tests (Portable Appliance Testing) needs to be carried out at least once a year and each lantern will display a sticker showing the date the lantern was tested. Check this date is within a year. The most important part of that test however, is the visual inspection. The lantern casing, cable and plug top should be visually inspected each time equipment is rigged which is quick and easy to do.

The following is a list of the general maintenance checks and preparation that need to be carried out for all lanterns before each rigging session:

- All colour filter (gel), gobos, irises etc should be removed.
- All lanterns must be fitted with a safety bond.
- All lanterns should have the appropriate size colour frame in the colour frame holder ready for the new filter
- The lantern tail (cable from lantern to plug) should be visually inspected for any cuts abrasions etc. and be firmly attached to the body of the lantern and into the mains plug
- The plug should be opened up and all connections checked to ensure they are firmly fastened to the appropriate terminal. The cable should be firmly secured with the cord grip so it cannot come loose.
- The lantern body should be checked for any defects. Any tape or black tack should be removed.
- Hook clamps should be correctly attached to the yoke and tightened so that they are still movable but not loose.
- Check that the tilt knob on the yoke holds the lamp body solidly when it is tightened as this is very important for focusing
- Lenses should be checked for defects, cracks, etc.

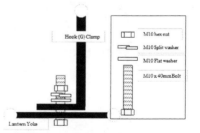

- The lanterns should be as clean and free of dust as possible. Use an air line to blow out any dust and wipe the lens with a clean damp cloth.
- All lanterns should be flash tested using a hot line at the end of inspection to ensure that they are functioning. Lamps will last longer if this is carried out though a dimmer at 40%.

In addition to the checks mentioned above there are specific checks for different types of lanterns.

Profiles

- Ensure that the two lenses move freely in their holders and that they can be tightened off.
- Each unit should have a set of four shutters; they should be able to move freely but firmly.
- Some profile units have a rotating lens tube. This should be able to move freely and set so the colour aperture at the front is topmost.

Fresnels and PCs

- All units should have the correct barndoors safely attached.
- All barndoors should be tight but able to move freely.
- Check that the focus knob moves freely and tightens.

Parcans

- Check that the bulb rotates in the lamp base so it can be focused
- If you have a lighting plan make sure the right beam angle lamp is in the parcan or the right lens is in a ETC Source Four PAR as this will save time on the fit up.

Matt Prentice

The rising Moon

Tips on Using Profile Spots

Using Frost in Profiles

Most profile lanterns are now 'cool beam' fixtures and use a dichroic reflector rather than an aluminium reflector. It is often not possible to achieve a soft enough focus with a profile for the purposes of general cover or as a colour wash.

To overcome this, a piece of light frost filter helps to soften the edges and either a piece of R132 or R119, both from Rosco, work well, turning the beam into something more like that given by a Fresnel lens.

These frost filters have become the industry standard used by most lighting designers across many venues to achieve this effect.

Focusing a Profile as a Wash Light

It is common to focus a profile with a sharp edge beam and then drop a frost filter into it achieve the soft focus required for a wash of light.

The frost filter should be inserted behind the colour frame, not in with the colour filter, so it may be removed easily before focusing the unit. Alternatively the frost can be put in the lantern as it is being focussed and not when the lighting rig is installed. This means the technician can work on a hard edge beam first before dropping in the frost filter.

Using Profiles as Back Light

Now that profile lanterns are available in very wide beam angles, such as the ETC's Source Four 70° or 90° or the Selecon Pacific 45° / 75° or 90°, they are very useful tools for area back light.

This can be especially handy when used in conjunction with colour changers. Colour changers often do not have slots to take a barn door so the profile shutters can be used to contain the light spill instead.

Profiles also allow hard edged or shuttered back light which enables the designer to define areas with hard focused squares or rectangles.

Because extra wide profiles are all 'cool beam' lanterns, the gel string in the colour changers last a lot longer without burning out or melting.

Very soft Fresnel-type back light can be achieved by soft focusing the profile and by adding some light frost filter into the lantern behind the colour changer in the second colour runner slot.

Moving Lights

In 1981 three sound engineers in the USA, not lighting people, developed the first moving light.

The first practical robotic light with built-in gobos was patented in 1983 by the company Showco of Dallas, Texas. That first light, known as the Vari*Lite VL1, had four overlapping internal wheels, three of which held round dichroic filters for colour changing.

Martin PAL 1200FX module with static and rotating gobos of metal, dichroic and textured glass.

Dichroic filters are made from specialised glass which had a succession of vacuum deposited layers, which selectively transmitted colour or block it. Pure bands of colour could be produced, with the practical benefit of high efficiency and stability at high temperature. The fourth wheel had varying diameter holes to control the projected beam diameter.

Later development gave pan and tilt control, hence the new generic term, moving head lights.

They have been called 'intelligent lights' but as someone once said: "If they were as intelligent as lighting designers, I could sit in the bar and let them get on with it, but they just do what they're programmed to do."

The precise beam angle control is particularly effective in fog – this projected as an expanding beam shower which could be rotated and swept about the stage like a giant bristle brush.

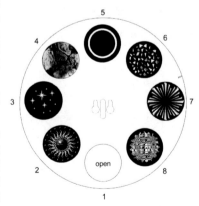

Vari-Lite diversified and prospered, and is now part of the giant Philips Group.

For many years there had been little major research by theatre lighting equipment manufacturers, and consequently little serious advance in lighting technology, but there was a potentially high reward for good lighting and effects in the worldwide club and

Gobo selection for the first High End Cyberlight.

touring market, and the rewards drove funded research. The results can be seen in the plethora of good products available today.

Following Vari-Lite, the Italian company Clay Paky was formed in 1976 by Pasquale Quadri and they developed a wide range of moving head lights and scanners, with their popular Sharpy compact moving head used widely in the Diamond Jubilee concert in London in the summer of 2012.

In 1987 Martin Professional was founded in Denmark and became a global supplier of a diverse family of lighting equipment.

In 1994 Robe Lighting in the Czech Republic was formed and has also developed into a world player.

- Some of the benefits of the research and development are listed below:
- Greater efficiency in control of a light beam from an instrument, both in precise reflection and lens system designs to produce beam control, focusing iris aperture and strobe facilities.
- The need for high efficiency light sources encouraged lamp makers to develop compact, long life high intensity discharge light sources, and later of course the ubiquitous LED light source.
- The need for high temperature colour media gave rise to the further development of the heat stable dichroic glass mentioned above, used initially by Vari-Lite and sophistication of wedge concept colour change.
- The improvements in optical design meant that more precision and resolution was demanded of gobos, and high temperatures meant heat stable materials for gobos, going from aluminium, phosphorbronze, stainless steel to glass – monochrome and then single and multicolour images and multiple gobos embedded in rotating wheels, with image morphing facilities.
- The need for fast, reliable, compact and quiet operation encouraged deeper research into motors and new generations of stepper motors were produced.

All the above factors gave more sophisticated control and better digital remote control systems emerged.

The diversity of elements that could be remotely controlled saw the emergence of the skilled lighting programmer.

In 2012 the trend was toward more compact, lighter weight, elegant external design look, and for more refined images and mid-air effects.

Typical colour wheel courtesy Robe Lighting.

Perhaps the most important feature of all this is that exciting commercially driven research and innovation drew talented people from other industries to fuel the development.

Operators' hands equate to motors.

LEDS: Light Emitting Diodes

These are a relatively recent development of a new light source that is replacing many familiar tungsten lamps. LEDs are very small, typically 2mm in diameter, light emitting elements that are usually mounted in a module or array, with control circuits to form a light fixture.

LEDs were introduced in 1997 and the technology is developing very quickly and continually. The efficiency, i.e. economic use of electricity continues to improve and capital costs reduce.

Most lighting companies now have LED fixtures and retro-fit kits for many areas of lighting, from street lighting, architectural and domestic lighting and now for the stage.

This is not the place for a long technical dissertation on LEDs, and it would need to be revised in a years' time so this summary of LED information and characteristics.

What is an LED?

An LED emits light when a controlled current passes through it via a control circuit. Each LED only emits a small amount of light, so they are usually formed into assemblies of LEDs to give the required amount of light.

Efficiency

LEDs have a much higher efficiency in converting electrical power to light, than the conventional tungsten lamp. Lumens are the unit of light quantity, and efficiency is measured in lumens per watt.

The final efficiency is the lumens per watt value that is emitted by the fixture. Tungsten lamps have an efficiency of 10-12 lumens per watt, and up to 30 lumens per watt for the more efficient tungsten halogen lamp.

LED efficiency is now over 100 lumens per watt and will continue to increase.

Colour

The small LEDs can be made in many colours, and can be selected to form a fixture to provide the wanted colour. Typical for architectural lighting, it may be 'daylight' or warm like the familiar tungsten lamp.

Also since LEDS can be made in colours Red and Green and Blue – RGB, approximate primary colours can be used and each colour connected in series, so that dimming can control the overall colour blend. Some companies assemble RGB plus Amber and White for better colour control, of sensitive flesh tones; others use seven colours to give even more control.

Quality of light

The generation of light from an LED is of a different nature to tungsten, which emits light, like any incandescent body, such as the sun, they have a 'continuous' spectrum, has all the colours of the rainbow in the simplest terms. LEDs emit a 'discontinuous' spectrum, with a spike in the blue (460nm) and a dip (500nm).

Because of this spiky nature of light emission, the colour may appear, for instance like tungsten, but will make objects look rather different. This is similar to the experience of looking at coloured objects under fluorescent lamps.

The lighting industry is trying to agree a reliable index metric to describe the colour rendering nature of LEDs.

Safety and Health

There is no ultra-violet (UV) energy or infra-red, (heat) from LEDs, and they operate at a low temperature.

There are some concerns over the 'blue spike' and experts are still evaluating it.

LED Disposal

There is no mercury content to LEDs as in fluorescent and some discharge lamps – these need to be disposed of in approved places – but LED disposal should be made in the same way, as there may be some trace materials that can be considered hazardous.

LED on-off Time

Like tungsten lamps, from the moment of switch on, full brightness is achieved instantly, as compared to fluorescent lamps which may take time to strike, and time to reach optimum light output.

LEDs can be restarted immediately without any delays, which may happen with some discharge lamps.

LED Life

A very long life, compared to all other light sources. The tungsten lamp generally has 1000 or 2000 hours, although some specialist lamps have a shorter higher light output life. Life for the tungsten lamp is defined as when 50% of a batch has failed.

LED life is claimed between 30,000 to 100,000 hours – remember that 24/7 burning time for a year is 8760 hours.

Life is not adversely affected by a rapid cycle of switching, as fluorescent may be. There is a slow fall in light output that is similar to the fluorescent lamp fade in life. Complete LED failure is unusual in the stated lifetime. They must be replaced by a specialist.

LED Temperature Dependence

LED light output is very sensitive to its immediate environment temperature and fixture makers, or installation teams must allow for airflow, and the assemblies have heat sinks and cooling fins to keep the LEDs at optimum light output.

Dimming

LED Systems can be dimmed without changing colour, although some systems can show 'stepping' at the lower end of dimming. Control may be by DMX via the lighting control desk.

Shock Resistance

Because LEDs are solid state devices, they are not easily damaged by physical shock.

Cost

Cost of units to give equivalent light output from a tungsten lamp of a given wattage, are high at present, but costs will fall steadily in the immediate and medium term future.

If annual usage is low, it is not easy to justify high cost if only small practical power cost savings are made.

Michael Hall

LED Profiles

The LED profile spot is an environmentally friendly alternative to a traditional tungsten profile. It is a more efficient light source than tungsten, therefore has lower running costs, but capital cost may be higher. This most recent of innovations combines all the advantages and familiarity of profile spot mechanics (gobo, shutter, iris and zoom capabilities, etc) with  a dimmable, economical, environmentally friendly light source.

Energy consumption is an issue which we are being forced to confront and power-saving across major areas of the industry is becoming increasingly important. Recent developments in LED technology have produced sources that are now powerful enough to be viable alternatives to tungsten, and improvements are being made all the time.

LED profiles vary between manufacturers but are available in different colour temperatures from cool, which may vary between manufacturers, warm and neutral white – there is as yet no standard, and colour and colour rendering may vary.

Colour changing is possible, but may not give the same potential colour potential as tungsten sources with appropriate colour filters. LEDs have different spectral characteristics to tungsten and filter companies offer gels to compensate. Television studios have been very quick to take up LED lighting as budgets force them to make stringent cuts. The long life of an LED light source combined with the profile spot gobo projection ability has also given LED profiles a new lease of life in the corporate and architectural worlds.

This is a technology very much in the development stage and worth watching for the future.

For more in depth information on LEDs see Michael Hall's overview on page 186.

Understanding Dimmers

Dimmers are an essential part of the presentation of a performance. They are one of the tools that enable lighting designers to make the audience look only in the right direction and hide the things that should not be seen. They make sunrises happen and turn night into day. But how do they work?

The electrical mains supply is a steady sinewave ready to be used. By varying the amount of electricity, the dimmer makes a light less or more bright. There are a number of types of dimmers in use in theatre which we shall investigate:

1. Forward Phase Dimming

This is the most common. Usually known as 'Triac Dimming' or 'Thyristor Dimming' it uses silicon electronic devices such as a pair of SCRs or a single Triac, to turn the mains waveform on part way through its cycle from the 'zero crossing point'.

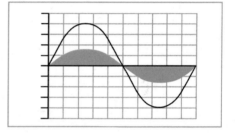

By varying the point in the cycle at which the electrical current turns on, we can alter the amount of power delivered to the lamp and hence the brightness. There are a number of advantages to forward phase dimming, as it is cheap, reliable, and well proven having basically worked in the same manner since the early 1960s. The technology is actually older than this being first developed in the 1930s using Thyratron valves.

Disadvantages of forward phase dimming include audible noise, electrical noise (harmonics) and inefficiency.

Noise in Forward Phase Dimming

The most noticeable source of noise in a forward phase dimming system is the filaments of the lamps being dimmed. This is sometimes referred to as 'lamp sing' or 'filament rattle'. When the power is turned on to the lamp part way through the mains cycle, the filament expands very rapidly, and then as the voltage ramps back down again the filament cools. At full or zero the filaments are silent. Some lamps produce more noise than others;

PAR 64 lamps are usually very noisy but will vary between manufacturers.

The noise can be lessened SCR and triac dimming systems by the use of chokes in the dimmer. A choke looks like a doughnut with wire wrapped around it. The choke has the effect of reducing the rate at which the current passes through the lamp. Chokes introduce 'rise time' measured in microseconds (µs) and is one of the factors in how much noise a lamp connected to a dimmer will make. Some types of lamp (such as PAR64) make much more noise than others (HPL,GKV) which are almost silent.

2. Reverse Phase Dimming

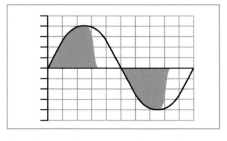

Reverse phase dimming takes the opposite approach to forward phase dimming and switches the sinewave off part way through the cycle from the zero-crossing point. Some architectural loads perform better this way, such as some fluorescent ballasts. It is very important when dimming a non-tungsten load to determine whether forward or reverse phase dimming is appropriate. Usually this information will be listed in the manufacturer's data sheet.

3. Sinewave Dimming

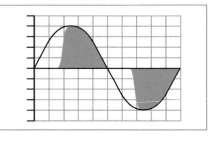

The previous versions of dimming discussed above both chop up the incoming mains supply each half cycle. This leads to noise in the filament as we have seen. Sinewave dimming was developed to not chop up the mains but to reduce the amplitude (size) whilst maintaining the same shape all the time in the same way that a volume control works on a radio or other piece of audio equipment. A Sinewave dimmer acts in a similar way to running a load via a variable transformer; a true variable voltage is supplied to the load. Sinewave dimming has many benefits including very low or silent lamp noise and lower power consumption, but is considerably more expensive to install initially.

What can I connect to a dimmer?

Some types of equipment must have a full sinewave from the mains supply to work properly and some also must have the full voltage so as not to be damaged. Almost without exception, motors will be damaged if connected to a dimmer, or worse, will also cause damage to the dimmer. Items with their own power supplies such as moving lights, computers and LED fixtures will invariably be damaged if connected to dimmers (often beyond economical repair). The simple rule is if it is not a tungsten light, check with the dimmer manufacturer or the manufacturer of the equipment to be connected.

Why will some pieces of equipment not turn off even though the dimmer is at zero level?

Two reasons here. The first is that dimmers usually need a minimum load connected to them to make them work. This is because the dimmer derives a tiny voltage from the load in order to make it work – that is to say, swap from the positive side of the cycle to the negative side of the mains supply cycle 50 or 60 times every second. If the load is too small, say in the case of a strobe light of a tiny motor on an effects wheel, the motor continues to turn and the strobe continues to flash. The second is that most theatre dimmers can be set to give a small output voltage that will keep filaments in tungsten lamps warm but invisible so as not to stress the filaments each time they are switched on from cold. This is known variously as pre-heat or 'bottom set' to stop premature (expensive) lamp failure. It is most important to note that placing a dimmer to zero on the control desk does not disconnect the output from the mains. The residual current is enough to give you a nasty electric shock and in some cases enough to give you a fatal electric shock, that is to say to electrocute you. Always disconnect a piece of equipment from a dimmer by pulling out the plug if there is any chance of you becoming connected to the mains input such as when changing a lamp.

Six-way 1 kW interlocking portable resistance dimmer unit, also made as a twelve-way.

Mark White

Lighting Desks

There are many types of lighting desk. They all however share one thing in common, they control individual channels both singly and in groups. A channel is one parameter, which can be a single dimmer that fades a stage light (luminaire) up and down, or can be many channels in one fixture such as a moving light that moves in many directions and can change colour and beam size. The channel is assigned a level, generally from zero to 100 where zero is off and 100 is full brightness.

Simple lighting desks have a fader or slider for each individual channel. These are usually arranged in rows and are numbered 1 to 12 or usually 1 to 24. These faders are subject to an overall control called a master or grand master that sets the overall output levels of the channels. The master thus enables all lights in a scene to be faded up and down together even if some of the channel faders are not set to full. These channels fade in proportion so that if a channel fader is set at say 60%, then a grand master setting of 50% takes that particular channel down to 30%. They all go off when the grand master is set to zero. We call that a blackout.

Some desks have two sets of channel faders, both labelled say 1 to 24. Each of these sets (or banks) of faders is also controlled by an individual master. If those particular masters 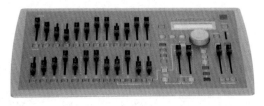 are set to zero, no light appears on stage. This enables the operator of the desk to preset that bank of faders in readiness for the next scene when one set of channel faders crossfades to another set of channel faders into the next scene. This type of desk would be called a 24 channel, 2 preset desk.

This type of simple lighting desk has no memory; it relies upon the operator presetting the next cue on the dark (or blind) bank of faders, performing a crossfade and resetting/presetting the faders on the bank that had just been in use. This can keep the operator very busy during a performance and can require a lot of concentration especially when the lighting cues follow rapidly on from each other.

More sophisticated desks have submasters which are also faders. These are programmed or loaded with groups of channels, say all the lights on a cyclorama or backdrop so that just one fader is required to bring those light up on stage, independent of the individual channel controls. It is quite possible to assign the same channels to more than one submaster; if the two submasters are in use at any one time the individual channel will be as bright as the higher of the two submaster levels. This however can give rise to a light on stage not going to blackout when the operator thought it should.

A desk that can recall lighting cues and play them back at the touch of a button is a memory desk. Individual channels or groups of channels and their levels are committed to a numbered memory. The memory numbers start at 1 and there are usually more than 100 memories in the smaller desks. The memories are usually known as cues and are generally played back sequentially from the lowest numbered cue.

The time taken for the changeover from one cue to the next is called the crossfade time and this time can be anywhere from zero seconds (a "snap" cue) to more than five minutes. On some desks, the cue fading out can have a different time to the cue fading in for special effects.

This illustration from James Cleaver's The Theatre at Work – a glimpse behind the scenes (Puffin), captures the ad-hoc combinations of lighting boards to be found on many backstage perches.

Power supply in the cellars of the Paris Opera. L'Illustration, (Paris), 18 June, 1887, p.432.

Fig 38 View of the 'electric room'. Nature, 11 (1875), 370.

196 Miscellany of Lighting & Stagecraft

ASSOCIATIONS

Association of British Theatre Technicians

The Association of British Theatre Technicians is a charity and a company limited by the guarantee of its members. It campaigns on behalf of the theatre industry to ensure legislation is appropriate to the industry's needs, and that regulations are suitably drafted and enforced.

Safety Helpline

ABTT provides a telephone and email enquiry service to help solve safety and technical problems for industry chat and difficult questions.

Training

ABTT runs training courses for technical and managerial skills; these include the Bronze, Silver and Gold Awards and specialist courses including Pyrotechnics and Risk Management.

Publications

The Association produces Sightline, the quarterly industry magazine for technical theatre, with news, reviews, features and Safety Matters. Other publications include the theatre industry's Codes of Practice specific to the industry's needs. ABTT also produces Technical Standards for Places of Entertainment in association with the District Surveyors Association and the Institute of Licensing. It also produces the Model National Conditions Guidance Notes on specific subjects are published when needed.

ABTT Theatre Show and Members' Events

ABTT organises the annual Theatre Show of backstage and front-of house equipment and supplies, and arranges visits, conferences, forums, lectures and meetings for members. Trips to interesting theatres and productions are arranged, frequently organised by ABTT NorthNet, the get-together of our members especially those north of Watford.

Committees

There are a number of highly influential committees, including Safety, Training, Theatre Planning and Historical Research. The Association also organises specialist interest groups such as the Production Managers Forum, which is a joint venture with the Stage Management Association.

OISTAT

The ABTT is the UK centre of OISTAT (International Organization of Scenographers, Theatre Architects and Technicians).

The Association of British Theatre Technicians
55 Farringdon Road, London, EC1M 3JB
Tel: +44 (0)20 7242 9200
Email: info@abtt.org.uk
Web: www.abtt.org.uk

Association of Lighting Designers

The Association of Lighting Designers is a professional body representing lighting designers working in the live performance industry in the United Kingdom and many other parts of the world.

Its aims are to further the art of lighting design and to raise the professional status of the Lighting Designer as a member of the creative team.

The majority of its members work in Theatre (including Opera and Dance), but there are many others working in Television, Architecture, Rock and Roll Concerts, Education and Corporate Presentation.

The ALD is the mouthpiece of the performance lighting industry and a resource for information on the wide range of lighting design topics that affect designers in the lighting profession.

Contact: PO Box 955, Southsea, PO1 9NF
Tel: 07817 060189
Email: office @ ald.org.uk
Web: www.ald.org.uk

National Skills Academy

The National Skills Academy for Creative & Cultural is a membership network of industry professionals working in partnership with 20 'Founder' further education colleges to develop and improve the skills landscape for the current and future workforce.

Contact: Lafone House, The Leathermarket, Weston Street,
London SE1 3HN
Tel: +44 (0)20 7015 1840
Email: nsa@ccskills.org.uk
Web: www.nsa-ccskills.co.uk

PLASA

PLASA is the lead international membership body for those who supply technologies and services to the event, entertainment and installation industries. As a pro-active trade association, it looks after the interests of its members and seeks to influence business practices and skills development across the industry.

Contact: Redoubt House, 1 Edward Road, Eastbourne, BN23 8AS
Tel: +44 (0)1323 524120
info.eu@plasa.org
www.plasa.org

Production Services Association

With over 1000 UK members, the Production Services Association represents the people and companies that provide technical services to live events. The PSA offers advice, lobbies on your behalf and consults with those that influence your industry. They work with insurers, help develop industry guidance and care passionately about the people that make amazing things happen.

Contact: PO Box 2709, Bath, Somerset BA1 3YS
Tel: +44 (0)1225 332668
Email: gm@psa.org.uk
Web: www.psa.co.uk

The Society of British Theatre Designers

The Society of British Theatre Designers is a professional organisation run by designers for the benefit of designers. It was created to benefit theatre designers and their profession and to explore and further the role of the designer within the arts today.

Contact: Theatre Design Department,
Rose Bruford College of Theatre and Performance,Burnt Oak Lane, Sidcup
DA15 9DF
Tel: +44 (0)20 8308 2664
Email: admin@theatredesign.org.uk
Web: www.theatredesign.org.uk

The Stage Management Association

The SMA is the national organisation for stage managers and those interested in stage management and other backstage work. All types of performances need great stage management, so they support, develop, represent and promote their members and the profession, with a wide range of services.

A free career guide to Stage Management can be downloaded from the website. Details of benefits of membership are also available alongside news and events, SMA Conference Reports and a Freelist which claims to be the ONLY up-to-date list of who is available for stage management work.

Contact: 89 Borough High Street, London SE1 1NL
Tel: +44 (0)20 7242 9250
Email: admin@stagemanagementassociation.co.uk
Web: www.stagemanagementassociation.co.uk

The Theatres Trust

The Theatres Trust is the National Advisory Body for Theatres, protecting theatres for everyone. It operates nationally in England, Wales, Scotland and Northern Ireland promoting the value of theatre buildings and championing their future.

The Trust provides a range of specialist advisory services to help theatres. It is a statutory consultee on planning applications and develops the debate on what makes a good theatre.

You can find out more about its work in 'About Us' on the Trust's website (see below).

Understand more about the Trust's Ecovenue initiative. Visit News & Planning for news coverage on theatres in the UK and planning applications or follow the Trust's work on Twitter or Like us on Facebook.

The Trust is also happy to respond to enquiries or requests for advice. Their Resource Centre Library is open to researchers by appointment. Read the Guide to using The Theatres Trust Resources and Resource Centre, find out about our Reference Library, or have a look at the Library Catalogue (Excel).

The Theatres Trust protects theatres for everyone. All donations, bequests and subscriptions go directly towards helping promote and protect theatres for future generations to enjoy. Join the Trust and become a part of theatres' future.

22 Charing Cross Road
London WC2H 0QL
Tel: 020 7836 8591
Email: info@theatrestrust.org.uk
Web: www.theatrestrust.org.uk

Women In Stage Entertainment (WISE)

WiSE is a networking and professional development organisation for women in the stage entertainment industry. Aimed at raising the profile of woken working in the industry, WiSE strives to provide a dynamic forum where members can share information, opportunities and support while promoting equity, equality, and sustainability across the industry.

Contact: 11 Old Steine, Brighton, East Sussex BN1 1EJ
Telephone: 01273 308584
Email: sarah@wiseonline.org
Web: www.wiseonline.org
Contacts: Sarah Rushton-Read, co-founder and director

Selected Publications

UK and USA

Amateur Stage www.asmagazine.co.uk

Entertainment Technology www.etnow.com

Lighting & Sound America www.lightingandsoundamerica.com

Lighting + Sound International www.lsionline.co.uk/magazine

Live Design livedesignonline.com

PLSN www.plsn.com

Sightline www.etnow.com/sightline

Total Production International www.tpimagazine.com

Worldwide

Actualité de la Scenographie (France) www.as-editions.fr

CX (Australia) www.juliusmedia.com

Etech Asia www.e-techasia.com

LAVA (Singapore) lavamagazine.com

Sono (France) www.sonomag.com

Sound & Stage Middle East www.digitalproductionme.com

SoundLightUP (France) www.soundlightup.com

VPLT Magazin (Germany) www.vplt-live.de

Chat rooms

The Blue Room www.blue-room.org.uk

UK Sound & LIght Community www.ukslc.org

APPENDIX

Common Acronyms in Current Use

ABTT	Association of British Theatre Technicians
ADCH	American Standard code for Information Interchange
ALD	Association of Lighting Designers
ALIA	Australian Lighting Industry Association
ASC	American Society of Cinematographers
ASD	Association of Sound Designers
ASM	Assistant Stage Manager
ASP	Association of Stage Pyro technicians
BECTU	Broadcasting, Entertainment, Cinematograph and Theatre Union – see their website for 'Jargon'
BS	British Standard
BSC	British Society of Cinematographers
BSI	British Standard Institution
BTR	Buhne Technica Rundschau
CC	Colour Compensating
CDM	Ceramic Discharge Metal halide Lamp
CE	Conformite European
CIBSE	Chartered Institute of Building Services Engineers (UK)
CID	Compact Iodide Discharge Lamp
CIE	Commission Internationale Eclairage
CITT	Canadian Institute for Theatre Technology
CP	Candlepower
CSI	Compact Source Iodide Lamp
CT	Colour Temperature
CTB	Colour Temperature Blue
CTO	Colour Temperature Orange
CTS	Colour Temperature Straw
CYM	Cyan Yellow and Magenta

DIN	Deutches Institut fur Norming E.V
DMX	Digital Multiplex – Common communication protocol in stage lighting
DSM	Deputy Stage Manager
ESTA	(North American) Entertainment Services and Technology Association – now merged with PLASA
FAQ	Frequently Asked Questions
FOH	Front of House
FX	Special Effects
HOD	Head of Development
HSE	Health and Safety Executive
HD	High Definition
HMI	Hydragyrum medium –arc Iodide Lamp
HPS	High Pressure Sodium Lamp
Hz	Hertz
IALD	International Association of Lighting Designers
IEE	Institute of Electrical Engineers
IR	Infra Red
ISCE	Institute of Sound and Communication Engineers
K	Kelvin
LASER	Light Amplification by the Stimulated Emission of Radiation
LSA	Lighting and Sound America (magazine)
LS&I	Lighting and Sound International (magazine)
Lm	Lumens
LDI	Lighting Dimensions International (magazine)
LED	Light Emitting Diode
MBI	Double ended metal halide lamp
MIRED	Micro Reciprocal Degrees
MSR	Medium Source Rare Earth Lamp
NCDT	National Council for Drama Training
ND	Neutral Density
ODEON	Oscar Deutz Entertains our Nation
OISTAT	International Organisation of Scenographers, Theatre

	Architects and Technicians
OLED	Organic Light Emitting Diode
PAR	Parabolic Aluminised Reflector
PD	Pebble Convex (lens)
PC	Piano Convex (or pebble convex) (lens)
PLASA	Professional Lighting and Sound Association
PM	Production Manager
PS/OP	Promptside Opposite Prompt (side)
PLSN	Projection Lighting and Staging News
RGB	Red Green Blue
RDM	Remote Device Management
SMPTE	Society of Motion Picture and Television Engineers (USA)
STLD	Society of Television Lighting Designers (UK)
SBTD	Society of British Theatre Designers
SX	Sound Effects
SMA	Stage Management Association
SL/SR	Stage Left / Stage Right
SM	Stage Manager
TH	Tungsten Halogen Lamp
USITT	United States Institute for Theatre Technology
UV	Ultraviolet
WEEE	Waste Electrical and Electronic Equipment
WISE	Women in Stage Entertainment

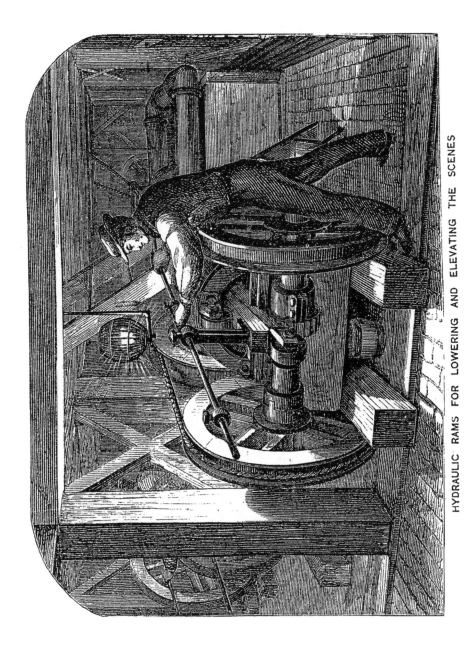

HYDRAULIC RAMS FOR LOWERING AND ELEVATING THE SCENES

ENTERTAINMENT TECHNOLOGY PRESS

FREE SUBSCRIPTION SERVICE

Keeping Up To Date with

Miscellany of lighting & Stagecraft

Entertainment Technology titles are continually up-dated, and all major changes and additions are listed in date order in the relevant dedicated area of the publisher's website. Simply go to the front page of www.etnow.com and click on the BOOKS button. From there you can locate the title and be connected through to the latest information and services related to the publication.

The content of this book is correct at the time of publishing, to the best of the authors' knowledge. We welcome suggestions and comments for future editions of the book, which should be addressed to roscomh@aol.com or julie@joolzharper.co.uk

Titles Published by Entertainment Technology Press

ABC of Theatre Jargon *Francis Reid* **£9.95** ISBN 9781904031093
This glossary of theatrical terminology explains the common words and phrases that are used in normal conversation between actors, directors, designers, technicians and managers.

Aluminium Structures in the Entertainment Industry *Peter Hind* **£24.95**
ISBN 9781904031062
Aluminium Structures in the Entertainment Industry aims to educate the reader in all aspects of the design and safe usage of temporary and permanent aluminium structures specific to the entertainment industry – such as roof structures, PA towers, temporary staging, etc.

AutoCAD 2010 – A Handbook for Theatre Users *David Ripley* **£24.95** ISBN 9781904031611
From 'Setting Up' to 'Drawing in Three Dimensions' via 'Drawings Within Drawings', this compact and fully illustrated guide to AutoCAD covers everything from the basics to full colour rendering and remote plotting. Title completely revised in June 2010.

Automation in the Entertainment Industry – A User's Guide *Mark Ager and John Hastie* **£29.95** ISBN 9781904031581
In the last 15 years, there has been a massive growth in the use of automation in entertainment, especially in theatres, and it is now recognised as its own discipline. However, it is still only used in around 5% of theatres worldwide. In the next 25 years, given current growth patterns, that figure will rise to 30%. This will mean that the majority of theatre personnel, including directors, designers, technical staff, actors and theatre management, will come into contact with automation for the first time at some point in their careers. This book is intended to provide insights and practical advice from those who use automation, to help the first-time user understand the issues and avoid the pitfalls in its implementation.

Basics – A Beginner's Guide to Lighting Design *Peter Coleman* **£9.95**
ISBN 9781904031413
The fourth in the author's 'Basics' series, this title covers the subject area in four main sections: The Concept, Practical Matters, Related Issues and The Design Into Practice. In an area that is difficult to be definitive, there are several things that cross all the boundaries of all lighting design and it's these areas that the author seeks to help with.

Basics – A Beginner's Guide to Special Effects *Peter Coleman* **£9.95**
ISBN 9781904031338
This title introduces newcomers to the world of special effects. It describes all types of special effects including pyrotechnic, smoke and lighting effects, projections, noise machines, etc. It places emphasis on the safe storage, handling and use of pyrotechnics.

Basics – A Beginner's Guide to Stage Lighting *Peter Coleman* **£9.95**
ISBN 9781904031208
This title does what it says: it introduces newcomers to the world of stage lighting. It will not teach the reader the art of lighting design, but will teach beginners much about the 'nuts and bolts' of stage lighting.

Basics: A Beginner's Guide to Stage Management *Peter Coleman* **£7.95**
ISBN 9781904031475
The fifth in Peter Coleman's popular 'Basics' series, this title provides a practical insight
into, and the definition of, the role of stage management. Further chapters describe Cueing
or 'Calling' the Show (the Prompt Book), and the Hardware and Training for Stage
Management. This is a book about people and systems, without which most of the technical
equipment used by others in the performance workplace couldn't function.

Basics – A Beginner's Guide to Stage Sound *Peter Coleman* **£9.95** ISBN 9781904031277
This title does what it says: it introduces newcomers to the world of stage sound. It will not
teach the reader the art of sound design, but will teach beginners much about the background
to sound reproduction in a theatrical environment.

Building Better Theaters *Michael Mell* **£16.95** 9781904031406
A title within our Consultancy Series, this book describes the process of designing a theater,
from the initial decision to build through to opening night. Michael Mell's book provides
a step-by-step guide to the design and construction of performing arts facilities. Chapters
discuss: assembling your team, selecting an architect, different construction methods, the
architectural design process, construction of the theater, theatrical systems and equipment,
the stage, backstage, the auditorium, ADA requirements and the lobby. Each chapter
clearly describes what to expect and how to avoid surprises. It is a must-read for architects,
planners, performing arts groups, educators and anyone who may be considering building or
renovating a theater.

Carry on Fading *Francis Reid* **£20.00** ISBN 9781904031642
This is a record of five of the best years of my life. Years so good that the only downside is
the pangs of guilt at enjoying such contentment in a world full of misery induced by greed,
envy and imposed ideologies. Fortunately my DNA is high on luck, optimism and blessing
counting. *Francis Reid.*

Case Studies in Crowd Management
Chris Kemp, Iain Hill, Mick Upton, Mark Hamilton **£16.95** ISBN 9781904031482
This important work has been compiled from a series of research projects carried out by
the staff of the Centre for Crowd Management and Security Studies at Buckinghamshire
Chilterns University College, and seminar work carried out in Berlin and Groningen with
partner Yourope. It includes case studies, reports and a crowd management safety plan for
a major outdoor rock concert, safe management of rock concerts utilising a triple barrier
safety system and pan-European Health & Safety Issues.

Case Studies in Crowd Management, Security and Business Continuity
Chris Kemp, Patrick Smith **£24.95** ISBN 9781904031635
The creation of good case studies to support work in progress and to give answers to those
seeking guidance in their quest to come to terms with perennial questions is no easy task.
The first Case Studies in Crowd Management book focused mainly on a series of festivals
and events that had a number of issues which required solving. This book focuses on a
series of events that had major issues that impacted on the every day delivery of the events
researched.

Close Protection – The Softer Skills *Geoffrey Padgham* **£11.95** ISBN 9781904031390
This is the first educational book in a new 'Security Series' for Entertainment Technology
Press, and it coincides with the launch of the new 'Protective Security Management'
Foundation Degree at Buckinghamshire Chilterns University College (BCUC). The author
is a former full-career Metropolitan Police Inspector from New Scotland Yard with 27
years' experience of close protection (CP). For 22 of those years he specialised in operations
and senior management duties with the Royalty Protection Department at Buckingham
Palace, followed by five years in the private security industry specialising in CP training
design and delivery. His wealth of protection experience comes across throughout the text,
which incorporates sound advice and exceptional practical guidance, subtly separating fact
from fiction. This publication is an excellent form of reference material for experienced
operatives, students and trainees.

A Comparative Study of Crowd Behaviour at Two Major Music Events
Chris Kemp, Iain Hill, Mick Upton **£7.95** ISBN 9781904031253
A compilation of the findings of reports made at two major live music concerts, and in
particular crowd behaviour, which is followed from ingress to egress.

Control Freak *Wayne Howell* **£28.95** ISBN 9781904031550
Control Freak is the second book by Wayne Howell. It provides an in depth study of
DMX512 and the new RDM (Remote Device Management) standards. The book is aimed
at both users and developers and provides a wealth of real world information based on the
author's twenty year experience of lighting control.

Copenhagen Opera House *Richard Brett and John Offord* **£32.00** ISBN 9781904031420
Completed in a little over three years, the Copenhagen Opera House opened with a royal gala
performance on 15th January 2005. Built on a spacious brown-field site, the building is a
landmark venue and this book provides the complete technical background story to an opera
house set to become a benchmark for future design and planning. Sixteen chapters by relevant
experts involved with the project cover everything from the planning of the auditorium and
studio stage, the stage engineering, stage lighting and control and architectural lighting through
to acoustic design and sound technology plus technical summaries.

Cue 80 *Francis Reid* **£17.95** ISBN 9781904031659
Although Francis Reid's work in theatre has been visual rather than verbal, writing has
provided crucial support. Putting words on paper has been the way in which he organised
and clarified his thoughts. And in his self-confessed absence of drawing skills, writing has
helped him find words to communicate his visual thinking in discussions with the rest of
the creative team. As a by-product, this process of searching for the right words to help
formulate and analyse ideas has resulted in half-a-century of articles in theatre journals.
Cue 80 is an anthology of these articles and is released in celebration of Francis' 80th
birthday.

Electrical Safety for Live Events *Marco van Beek* **£16.95** ISBN 9781904031284
This title covers electrical safety regulations and good pracitise pertinent to the
entertainment industries and includes some basic electrical theory as well as clarifying the
"do's and don't's" of working with electricity.

Entertainment in Production Volume 1: 1994-1999 *Rob Halliday* **£24.95**
ISBN 9781904031512

Entertainment in Production Volume 2: 2000-2006 *Rob Halliday* **£24.95**
ISBN 9781904031529
Rob Halliday has a dual career as a lighting designer/programmer and author and in these two volumes he provides the intriguing but comprehensive technical background stories behind the major musical productions and other notable projects spanning the period 1994 to 2005. Having been closely involved with the majority of the events described, the author is able to present a first-hand and all-encompassing portrayal of how many of the major shows across the past decade came into being. From *Oliver!* and *Miss Saigon* to *Mamma Mia!* and *Mary Poppins*, here the complete technical story unfolds. The books, which are profusely illustrated, are in large part an adapted selection of articles that first appeared in the magazine *Lighting&Sound International*.

Entertainment Technology Yearbook 2008 *John Offord* **£14.95** ISBN 9781904031543
The new Entertainment Technology Yearbook 2008 covers the year 2007 and includes picture coverage of major industry exhibitions in Europe compiled from the pages of Entertainment Technology magazine and the etnow.com website, plus articles and pictures of production, equipment and project highlights of the year. Also included is a major European Trade Directory that will be regularly updated on line. A new edition will be published each year at the ABTT Theatre Show in London in June.

The Exeter Theatre Fire *David Anderson* **£24.95** ISBN 9781904031130
This title is a fascinating insight into the events that led up to the disaster at the Theatre Royal, Exeter, on the night of September 5th 1887. The book details what went wrong, and the lessons that were learned from the event.

Fading Light – A Year in Retirement *Francis Reid* **£14.95** ISBN 9781904031352
Francis Reid, the lighting industry's favourite author, describes a full year in retirement. "Old age is much more fun than I expected," he says. Fading Light describes visits and experiences to the author's favourite theatres and opera houses, places of relaxation and re-visits to scholarly institutions.

Focus on Lighting Technology *Richard Cadena* **£17.95** ISBN 9781904031147
This concise work unravels the mechanics behind modern performance lighting and appeals to designers and technicians alike. Packed with clear, easy-to-read diagrams, the book provides excellent explanations behind the technology of performance lighting.

The Followspot Guide *Nick Mobsby* **£28.95** ISBN 9781904031499
The first in ETP's Equipment Series, Nick Mobsby's Followspot Guide tells you everything you need to know about followspots, from their history through to maintenance and usage. It's pages include a technical specification of 193 followspots from historical to the latest 2007 versions from major manufacturers.

From Ancient Rome to Rock 'n' Roll – a Review of the UK Leisure Security Industry
Mick Upton **£14.95** ISBN 9781904031505
From stewarding, close protection and crowd management through to his engagement as

a senior consultant Mick Upton has been ever present in the events industry. A founder of ShowSec International in 1982 he was its chairman until 2000. The author has led the way on training within the sector. He set up the ShowSec Training Centre and has acted as a consultant at the Bramshill Police College. He has been prominent in the development of courses at Buckinghamshire New University where he was awarded a Doctorate in 2005. Mick has received numerous industry awards. His book is a personal account of the development and professionalism of the sector across the past 50 years.

Gobos for Image Projection *Michael Hall and Julie Harper* **£25.95**
ISBN 9781904031628
In this first published book dedicated totally to the gobo, the authors take the reader through from the history of projection to the development of the present day gobo. And there is broad practical advice and ample reference information to back it up. A feature of the work is the inclusion, interspersed throughout the text, of comment and personal experience in the use and application of gobos from over 25 leading lighting designers worldwide.

Health and Safety Aspects in the Live Music Industry *Chris Kemp, Iain Hill* **£30.00**
ISBN 9781904031222
This title includes chapters on various safety aspects of live event production and is written by specialists in their particular areas of expertise.

Health and Safety Management in the Live Music and Events Industry *Chris Hannam* **£25.95** ISBN 9781904031307
This title covers the health and safety regulations and their application regarding all aspects of staging live entertainment events, and is an invaluable manual for production managers and event organisers.

Hearing the Light – 50 Years Backstage *Francis Reid* **£24.95** ISBN 9781904031185
This highly enjoyable memoir delves deeply into the theatricality of the industry. The author's almost fanatical interest in opera, his formative period as lighting designer at Glyndebourne and his experiences as a theatre administrator, writer and teacher make for a broad and unique background.

An Introduction to Rigging in the Entertainment Industry *Chris Higgs* **£24.95**
ISBN 9781904031123
This book is a practical guide to rigging techniques and practices and also thoroughly covers safety issues and discusses the implications of working within recommended guidelines and regulations. Second edition revised September 2008.

Let There be Light – Entertainment Lighting Software Pioneers in Conversation *Robert Bell* **£32.00** ISBN 9781904031246
Robert Bell interviews a distinguished group of software engineers working on entertainment lighting ideas and products.

Light and Colour Filters *Michael Hall and Eddie Ruffell* **£23.95** ISBN 9781904031598
Written by two acknowledged and respected experts in the field, this book is destined to become the standard reference work on the subject. The title chronicles the development and use of colour filters and also describes how colour is perceived and how filters function.

Up-to-date reference tables will help the practitioner make better and more specific choices of colour.

Lighting for Roméo and Juliette *John Offord* **£26.95** ISBN 9781904031161
John Offord describes the making of the Vienna State Opera production from the lighting designer's viewpoint – from the point where director Jürgen Flimm made his decision not to use scenery or sets and simply employ the expertise of LD Patrick Woodroffe.

Lighting Systems for TV Studios *Nick Mobsby* **£45.00** ISBN 9781904031000
Lighting Systems for TV Studios, now in its second edition, is the first book specifically written on the subject and has become the 'standard' resource work for studio planning and design covering the key elements of system design, luminaires, dimming, control, data networks and suspension systems as well as detailing the infrastructure items such as cyclorama, electrical and ventilation. Sensibly TV lighting principles are explained and some history on TV broadcasting, camera technology and the equipment is provided to help set the scene! The second edition includes applications for sine wave and distributed dimming, moving lights, Ethernet and new cool lamp technology.

Lighting Techniques for Theatre-in-the-Round *Jackie Staines* **£24.95**
ISBN 9781904031017
Lighting Techniques for Theatre-in-the-Round is a unique reference source for those working on lighting design for theatre-in-the-round for the first time. It is the first title to be published specifically on the subject, it also provides some anecdotes and ideas for more challenging shows, and attempts to blow away some of the myths surrounding lighting in this format.

Lighting the Diamond Jubilee Concert *Durham Marenghi* **£19.95** ISBN 9781904031673
In this highly personal landmark document the show's lighting designer Durham Marenghi pays tribute to the team of industry experts who each played an important role in bringing the Diamond Jubilee Concert to fruition, both for television and live audiences. The book contains colour production photography throughout and describes the production processes and the thinking behind them. In his Foreword, BBC Executive Producer Guy Freeman states: "Working with the whole lighting team on such a special project was a real treat for me and a fantastic achievement for them, which the pages of this book give a remarkable insight into."

Lighting the Stage *Francis Reid* **£14.95** ISBN 9781904031086
Lighting the Stage discusses the human relationships involved in lighting design – both between people, and between these people and technology. The book is written from a highly personal viewpoint and its 'thinking aloud' approach is one that Francis Reid has used in his writings over the past 30 years.

Miscellany of Lighting and Stagecraft *Michael Hall & Julie Harper* **£22.95**
ISBN 9781904031680
This title will help schools, colleges, amateurs, technicians and all those interested in practical theatre and performance to understand, in an entertaining and informative way, the key backstage skills. Within its pages, numerous professionals share their own special knowledge and expertise, interspersed with diversions of historic interest and anecdotes

from those practising at the front line of the industry. As a result, much of the advice and skills set out have not previously been set in print. The editors' intention with this book is to provide a Miscellany that is not ordered or categorised in strict fashion, but rather encourages the reader to flick through or dip into it, finding nuggets of information and anecdotes to entertain, inspire and engender curiosity – also to invite further research or exploration and generally encourage people to enter the industry and find out for themselves.

Model National Standard Conditions *ABTT/DSA/LGLA* **£20.00** ISBN 9781904031116
These *Model National Standard Conditions* covers operational matters and complement *The Technical Standards for Places of Entertainment*, which describes the physical requirements for building and maintaining entertainment premises.

Mr Phipps' Theatre *Mark Jones, John Pick* **£17.95** ISBN: 9781904031383
Mark Jones and John Pick describe "The Sensational Story of Eastbourne's Royal Hippodrome" – formerly Eastbourne Theatre Royal. An intriguing narrative, the book sets the story against a unique social history of the town. Peter Longman, former director of The Theatres Trust, provides the Foreword.

Northen Lights *Michael Northen* **£17.95** ISBN 9781904031666
Many books have been written by famous personalities in the theatre about their lives and work. However this is probably one of the first memoirs by someone who has spent his entire career behind scenes, and not in front of the footlights. As a lighting designer and as consultant to designers and directors, Michael Northen worked through an exciting period of fifty years of theatrical history from the late nineteen thirties in theatres in the UK and abroad, and on productions ranging from Shakespeare, opera and ballet to straight plays, pantomimes and cabaret. This is not a complicated technical text book, but is intended to give an insight into some of the 300 productions in which he had been involved and some of the directors, the designers and backstage staff he have worked with, viewed from a new angle.

Pages From Stages *Anthony Field* **£17.95** ISBN 9781904031260
Anthony Field explores the changing style of theatres including interior design, exterior design, ticket and seat prices, and levels of service, while questioning whether the theatre still exists as a place of entertainment for regular theatre-goers.

Performing Arts Technical Training Handbook 2009/2010 *ed: John Offord* **£19.95**
ISBN 9781904031604
Published in association with the ABTT (Association of British Theatre Technicians), this important Handbook includes fully detailed and indexed entries describing courses on backstage crafts offered by over 100 universities and colleges across the UK. A completely new research project, with accompanying website, the title also includes articles with advice for those considering a career 'behind the scenes', together with contact information and descriptions of the major organisations involved with industry training – plus details of companies offering training within their own premises. The Handbook will be kept in print, with a major revision annually.

Practical Dimming *Nick Mobsby* **£22.95** ISBN 97819040313444
This important and easy to read title covers the history of electrical and electronic dimming, how dimmers work, current dimmer types from around the world, planning of a dimming

system, looking at new sine wave dimming technology and distributed dimming. Integration of dimming into different performance venues as well as the necessary supporting electrical systems are fully detailed. Significant levels of information are provided on the many different forms and costs of potential solutions as well as how to plan specific solutions. Architectural dimming for the likes of hotels, museums and shopping centres is included. Practical Dimming is a companion book to Practical DMX and is designed for all involved in the use, operation and design of dimming systems.

Practical DMX *Nick Mobsby* **£16.95** ISBN 9781904031369
In this highly topical and important title the author details the principles of DMX, how to plan a network, how to choose equipment and cables, with data on products from around the world, and how to install DMX networks for shows and on a permanently installed basis. The easy style of the book and the helpful fault finding tips, together with a review of different DMX testing devices provide an ideal companion for all lighting technicians and system designers. An introduction to Ethernet and Canbus networks are provided as well tips on analogue networks and protocol conversion. This title has been recently updated to include a new chapter on Remote Device Management that became an international standard in Summer 2006.

Practical Guide to Health and Safety in the Entertainment Industry
Marco van Beek **£14.95** ISBN 9781904031048
This book is designed to provide a practical approach to Health and Safety within the Live Entertainment and Event industry. It gives industry-pertinent examples, and seeks to break down the myths surrounding Health and Safety.

Production Management *Joe Aveline* **£17.95** ISBN 9781904031109
Joe Aveline's book is an in-depth guide to the role of the Production Manager, and includes real-life practical examples and 'Aveline's Fables' – anecdotes of his experiences with real messages behind them.

Rigging for Entertainment: Regulations and Practice *Chris Higgs* **£19.95**
ISBN 9781904031215
Continuing where he left off with his highly successful *An Introduction to Rigging in the Entertainment Industry*, Chris Higgs' second title covers the regulations and use of equipment in greater detail.

Rock Solid Ethernet *Wayne Howell* **£23.95** ISBN 9781904031697
Now in its third edition, *Rock Solid Ethernet* is aimed specifically at specifiers, installers and users of entertainment industry systems, this book will give the reader a thorough grounding in all aspects of computer networks, whatever industry they may work in. The inclusion of historical and technical 'sidebars' make for an enjoyable as well as an informative read.

Sixty Years of Light Work *Fred Bentham* **£26.95** ISBN 9781904031079
This title is an autobiography of one of the great names behind the development of modern stage lighting equipment and techniques.

Sound for the Stage *Patrick Finelli* **£24.95** ISBN 9781904031154
Patrick Finelli's thorough manual covering all aspects of live and recorded sound for performance is a complete training course for anyone interested in working in the field of stage sound, and is a must for any student of sound.

Stage Automation *Anton Woodward* **£12.95** ISBN 9781904031567
The purpose of this book is to explain the stage automation techniques used in modern theatre to achieve some of the spectacular visual effects seen in recent years. The book is targeted at automation operators, production managers, theatre technicians, stage engineering machinery manufacturers and theatre engineering students. Topics are covered in sufficient detail to provide an insight into the thought processes that the stage automation engineer has to consider when designing a control system to control stage machinery in a modern theatre. The author has worked on many stage automation projects and developed the award-winning Impressario stage automation system.

Stage Lighting Design in Britain: The Emergence of the Lighting Designer, 1881-1950 *Nigel Morgan* **£17.95** ISBN 9781904031345
This book sets out to ascertain the main course of events and the controlling factors that determined the emergence of the theatre lighting designer in Britain, starting with the introduction of incandescent electric light to the stage, and ending at the time of the first public lighting design credits around 1950. The book explores the practitioners, equipment, installations and techniques of lighting design.

Stage Lighting for Theatre Designers *Nigel Morgan* **£17.95** ISBN 9781904031192
This is an updated second edition of Nigel Morgan's popular book for students of theatre design – outlining all the techniques of stage lighting design.

Technical Marketing Techniques *David Brooks, Andy Collier, Steve Norman* **£24.95** ISBN 9781904031031
Technical Marketing is a novel concept, recently defined and elaborated by the authors of this book, with business-to-business companies competing in fast developing technical product sectors.

Technical Standards for Places of Entertainment *ABTT/DSA* **£45.00** ISBN 9781904031536
Technical Standards for Places of Entertainment details the necessary physical standards required for entertainment venues. New A4 revised edition June 2008.

Theatre Engineering and Stage Machinery *Toshiro Ogawa* **£30.00** ISBN 9781904031024
Theatre Engineering and Stage Machinery is a unique reference work covering every aspect of theatrical machinery and stage technology in global terms, and across the complete historical spectrum. Revised February 2007.

Theatre Lighting in the Age of Gas *Terence Rees* **£24.95** ISBN 9781904031178
Entertainment Technology Press has republished this valuable historic work previously produced by the Society for Theatre Research in 1978. *Theatre Lighting in the Age of Gas*

investigates the technological and artistic achievements of theatre lighting engineers from the 1700s to the late Victorian period.

Theatre Space: A Rediscovery Reported *Francis Reid* **£19.95** ISBN 9781904031437
In the post-war world of the 1950s and 60s, the format of theatre space became a matter for a debate that aroused passions of an intensity unknown before or since. The proscenium arch was clearly identified as the enemy, accused of forming a barrier to disrupt the relations between the actor and audience. An uneasy fellow-traveller at the time, Francis Reid later recorded his impressions whilst enjoying performances or working in theatres old and new and this book is an important collection of his writings in various theatrical journals from 1969-2001 including his contribution to the Cambridge Guide to the Theatre in 1988. It reports some of the flavour of the period when theatre architecture was rediscovering its past in a search to establish its future.

Theatres of Achievement *John Higgins* **£29.95** ISBN: 9781904031376
John Higgins affectionately describes the history of 40 distinguished UK theatres in a personal tribute, each uniquely illustrated by the author. Completing each profile is colour photography by Adrian Eggleston.

Theatric Tourist *Francis Reid* **£19.95** ISBN 9781904031468
Theatric Tourist is the delightful story of Francis Reid's visits across more than 50 years to theatres, theatre museums, performances and even movie theme parks. In his inimitable style, the author involves the reader within a personal experience of venues from the Legacy of Rome to theatres of the Renaissance and Eighteenth Century Baroque and the Gustavian Theatres of Stockholm. His performance experiences include Wagner in Beyreuth, the Pleasures of Tivoli and Wayang in Singapore. This is a 'must have' title for those who are as "incurably stagestruck" as the author.

Through the Viewfinder *Jeremy Hoare* **£21.95** ISBN: 9781904031574
Do you want to be a top television cameraman? Well this is going to help!
Through the Viewfinder is aimed at media students wanting to be top professional television cameramen – but it will also be of interest to anyone who wants to know what goes on behind the cameras that bring so much into our homes.
The author takes his own opinionated look at how to operate a television camera based on 23 years' experience looking through many viewfinders for a major ITV network company. Based on interviews with people he has worked with, all leaders in the profession, the book is based on their views and opinions and is a highly revealing portrait of what happens behind the scenes in television production from a cameraman's point of view.

Walt Disney Concert Hall – The Backstage Story *Patricia MacKay & Richard Pilbrow* **£28.95** ISBN 9781904031239
Spanning the 16-year history of the design and construction of the Walt Disney Concert Hall, this book provides a fresh and detailed behind the scenes story of the design and technology from a variety of viewpoints. This is the first book to reveal the "process" of the design of a concert hall.

Yesterday's Lights – A Revolution Reported *Francis Reid* **£26.95** ISBN 9781904031321
Set to help new generations to be aware of where the art and science of theatre lighting is
coming from – and stimulate a nostalgia trip for those who lived through the period, Francis
Reid's latest book has over 350 pages dedicated to the task, covering the 'revolution' from
the fifties through to the present day. Although this is a highly personal account of the
development of lighting design and technology and he admits that there are 'gaps', you'd be
hard put to find anything of significance missing.

*Go to www.etbooks.co.uk for full details of above titles and secure online ordering facilities.
All books also available on Kindle.*